Civil Engineering Heritage
Southern England

£2-75

Ouse Viaduct. Courtesy of Aerofilms Ltd

Civil Engineering Heritage
Southern England

Edited by R. A. Otter, BSc, CEng, MICE

Other books in the Civil Engineering Heritage series:
Northern England. Edited by M. F. Barbey.
Wales and Western England. Edited by W. J. Sivewright
Eastern and Central England. Edited by E. A. Labrum

Future titles in the series:
Scotland
Ireland
London

Southern England
Published for the Institution of Civil Engineers by Thomas Telford Ltd,
Thomas Telford House, 1 Heron Quay, London E14 4JD

First published 1994

A CIP record exists for this book

ISBN 07277 1971 8

Typeset in Palatino 10/11.5 using Ventura 4 at Thomas Telford Services Ltd
Printed in Great Britain by Galliard (Printers) Ltd, Great Yarmouth, Norfolk

Alan G. Allnutt, BSc (Eng), CEng,FICE

(1909–1989)

Alan Allnutt spent the majority of his professional life associated with the maintenance and development of civil engineering works related to Naval Dockyards, both in the United Kingdom and overseas. During his long retirement, in particular, he was able to devote significant time to the pursuit of his long-standing interest in civil engineering history. He acquired an outstanding knowledge of many aspects of the subject, and both through his association with the Institution of Civil Engineers' Panel for Historical Engineering Works and a wide range of other activities, he greatly contributed to the subject's understanding. He joined the Panel in 1973 and remained an active member until his decease at the age of 80.

In 1984 he was invited to be the editor of this volume — a role which he undertook with characteristic enthusiasm. In association with others he was responsible for planning the outline and structure of this volume and was also personally responsible for much of the basic research work and initial drafts of the sections relating to Dorset, Hampshire and Sussex. Both nationally and locally he was a much respected figure by those who shared his enthusiasm for engineering history.

This volume is dedicated to his memory.

Series Production Editor and Designer: Sally M. Smith

Front cover: Eddystone Lighthouse by R. B. Beechey. Reproduced by kind permission
of the Corporation of Trinity House

Title page: West Pier, Brighton

Preface

In 1971 the Institution of Civil Engineers set up the Panel for Historical Engineering Works to compile a library of records of civil engineering works of interest throughout the British Isles. The works covered by these records have been selected for their technical interest, innovation, durability or visual attraction. This archive has become the principal national repository for records of civil engineering works and is now regarded as the leading authority on such works. Although the modern profession of civil engineering can be reasonably dated from the foundation of the ICE in 1818, the record contains many older works with a few, like Stonehenge, of great antiquity. The series *Civil Engineering Heritage* seeks to make available to a wider public information contained in this archive, together with research undertaken by the Institution of Civil Engineers' Panel for Historical Engineering Works.

A civil engineer may be described as having responsibility for the design, construction and maintenance of a nation's infrastructure. Thus civil engineers have been at the forefront in the provision of transport systems whether they be canals, railways, roads or motorways in addition to harbours and airports associated with sea and air travel. They play the dominant role in the provision of water supply and sewer systems, which remain the principal defence against a range of epidemic diseases. Other works commonly undertaken by civil engineers include the construction of power stations and offshore structures for the oil and gas industries, water resource management including flood alleviation, coastal management and sea defence schemes, aspects of mineral extraction, town centre developments and the construction of a very wide range of industrial and domestic buildings.

The Editor would like to thank the following members of the Institution of Civil Engineers' Panel for Historical Engineering Works, who have been the principal contributors to this volume: D. J. Greenfield, H. E. M. Eagles and A. B. George, assisted by R. P. Truscott, together with former Panel members D. Shennan, A. T. Russell, W. J. Sivewright and especially A. G. Allnutt whose contribution is described elsewhere. Former Panel

Vice-Chairman, M. F. Barbey made important contributions during the earlier stages of development. The Panel's current Vice-Chairman and former Technical Secretary, T. B. O'Loughlin has freely given of his time, experience and knowledge of civil engineering history and has greatly assisted the book's progress especially over its later stages of production. Panel Chairman, R. A. Paxton and his predecessor, Professor A. W. Skempton have provided appropriate advice and encouragement.

Thanks are due to the Ordnance Survey for their permission to reproduce the maps and to staff of British Rail, Trinity House, local authorities, public utilities and others who have provided both help and encouragement. Great assistance has been given by the Institution of Civil Engineers' Archivist, Mrs M. Murphy and Chief Librarian, Mr M. M. Chrimes, together with other members of the library staff including Carol Arrowsmith who helped to type the draft text. Thanks are also due to Mrs V. Witherington and Mrs J. Johnston for their assistance in this task and to Dr James H. Thomas, of the University of Portsmouth for his constructive comments.

Bob Otter

Contents

The area covered by this volume

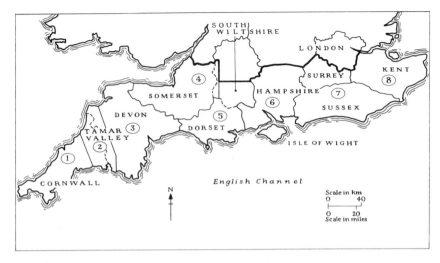

1. The Scilly Isles, West & Central Cornwall
2. The Tamar Valley & Plymouth
3. Central & Eastern Devon
4. Somerset & Mid-Wiltshire

5. Dorset and South Wiltshire
6. Hampshire and Isle of Wight
7. Sussex and South Surrey
8. Kent

Access to sites

Additional information relating to site accessibility has been included in some individual item descriptions. Also shown, adjacent to item headings, is one of the following three symbols providing simple guidance to accessibility.

♣   may be visited and viewed relatively easily. In some cases an entrance fee may be payable.

♦ access to the whole or important parts of these works is difficult. In some cases these works are on private land, within secure areas of Government property or part of a working industrial complex. In other cases the works are in remote geographical locations and a few have been demolished.

♠ identifies works which extend over wide areas such as road, railway and canal route items and some areas of drainage or reclamation.

This information was compiled in good faith on information available to the publishers at the time of going to press. They accept no responsibility for any inaccuracies or for subsequent changes in the status of sites.

Introduction

This volume covers Southern England from Cornwall to Kent and northwards to Somerset and parts of Wiltshire and Surrey. As with the companion volumes, each section relates to a defined geographical area mainly based on county boundaries. A map, a list of the described sites and a brief introduction are provided for each. The Historical Engineering Work (HEW) number under which a work is registered in the Institution of Civil Engineers' archives is also is given for each site.

References for individual items are included and there is appended a selective bibliography relating to more general aspects of the history of civil engineering. The sites' Ordnance Survey national grid reference is also provided together with a site access guide, which together with the geographical ordering of the items is designed to facilitate site visits. Although public access has been a factor in the selection of items for inclusion in this volume, regrettably a minority cannot be easily viewed.

The process of selecting appropriate items is not without its difficulties. Some works like Smeaton's Eddystone Tower and Brunel's Tamar Bridge are of international renown and could not possibly be excluded. Others, however, may in themselves be of considerably lesser significance, yet they are typical examples of, for example, a particular structural form, a distinctive use of a material or a construction technique. All, however large or small, have been selected with the intent of illustrating some aspect of the historic development of engineering skills or the scope of activity undertaken by the civil engineering profession.

It is hoped that both those with an engineering background and the more general reader will be assisted by this volume in better understanding the contribution made by the civil engineering profession in respect of the nation's economic development and day to day convenience and will gain greater insight into the diversity of expertise and experience which has contributed to our civil engineering heritage.

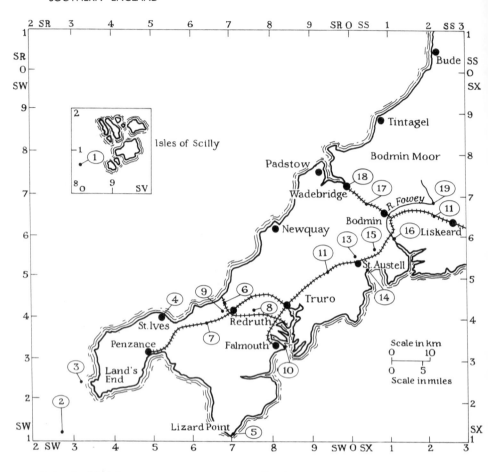

1. Bishop Rock Lighthouse
2. Wolf Rock Lighthouse
3. Longships Lighthouse
4. Smeaton's Pier, St Ives
5. Lizard Lighthouse
6. Early Tram-roads
7. The West Cornwall Railway
8. The Great County Adit
9. East Pool Pump and Whim
10. Falmouth Port

11. The Cornwall Railway
12. Timber railway viaducts (various sites not shown)
13. Wheal Martyn Water Wheel
14. Charlestown Harbour
15. Treffry Viaduct
16. Lostwithiel Bridge
17. Bodmin and Wadebridge Railway
18. Wadebridge, Ancient Bridge
19. Treverbyn Bridge

1. The Scilly Isles, West and Central Cornwall

Cornwall is characterised by a long and generally very rugged coastline, which has proved treacherous to mariners throughout the centuries. Lighthouses, both those on-shore, like that at the Lizard, and those marking individual off-shore rocks, like Bishop Rock, are necessary and notable features. The Fal estuary, one of the nation's finest natural harbours, is the first major refuge encountered by ships proceeding up the English Channel. Although of great local importance, the national role of the Fal estuary has been hampered by its geographical remoteness from London and major industrial centres. Many other small, often picturesque, harbours, like St Ives, are located around the coast; these were constructed to serve local community needs and to support Cornwall's mineral extraction industries. A series of harbours, including Charlestown on the peninsula's south-east coast, have been closely associated with the export of china clay, which remains a thriving industry. In mid-Cornwall the 'white mountains' of tipped micaceous sand resulting from clay extraction used to be a dominant topographical feature but are now landscaped and seeded.

Mineral extraction, including copper and tin, has occurred over very many centuries. There is evidence that the Phoenicians traded in Cornish minerals but mining has dramatically declined in recent years. The mines required extensive drainage works like the Great County Adit and the development and use of steam engines for pumping and winding. Notable features of Cornwall's landscape are the ruins of numerous pump and winding engine houses which are typified by the buildings and machinery at East Pool.

Cornwall's transport system has developed both to serve local needs and to provide links with the remainder of the country. A number of bridges of medieval origin, like Treverbyn or Wadebridge, which illustrate the traditional road network, still remain. Canals made little impact in Cornwall but a number of tram-roads, like that between Poldice and Portreath, were developed in the early nineteenth century principally to provide more efficient transport links from the mining areas to the coast. These, in turn, were superseded by the railway network. Cornwall's first steam traction line, the Bodmin and Wadebridge, was built for the carriage of minerals, as was the Hayle Railway. This was taken over by the standard gauge West Cornwall which, along with the broad gauge Cornwall Railway, was to connect the county to the national rail network. It was in 1859, with the opening of the Royal Albert Bridge, Cornwall's railway gateway, that a route into and through Cornwall was possible. Actual through running to Penzance was not possible until 1866 when a third rail was laid on the West Cornwall Railway. Tunnels are not a common feature of the network but there are a number of impressive structures like Treffry Viaduct. The numerous timber viaducts, now replaced by other structures, are held to be good examples of I. K. Brunel's engineering skill.

Rainfall is plentiful. Unlike parts of Wales and Cumbria where some large reservoirs supply remote population centres, Cornish reservoirs are relatively small and have been designed to serve the needs of local communities.

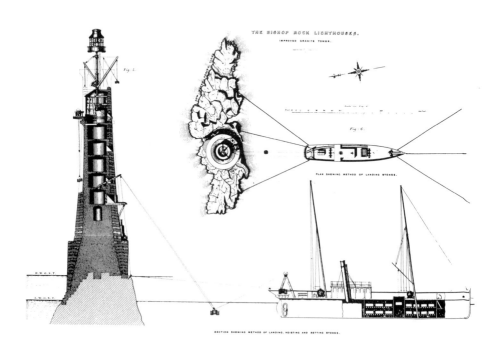

The Bishop Rock Lighthouse, 1891, from *Min. Proc. Instn Civ. Engrs*, **108**, 1891–92

1. Bishop Rock Lighthouse

◆

HEW 75

SV 807 064

Bishop Rock is 4 miles west of the southern tip of St Agnes, the most southerly inhabited island of the Scilly group. It is of hard pink granite and forms a small island at low water. Severe Atlantic storms are capable of throwing spray and stones 100 ft into the air. In 1707 the rock was the scene of a major disaster to a naval squadron under the command of Sir Clowdisley Shovell, who perished when his flagship and two other ships struck the rock and Clerk Rock and were lost. During the first half of the twentieth century the lighthouse was the eastern starting and finishing mark for the competition between the large passenger liners for the Blue Riband of the Atlantic.

In 1847 work began on the first lighthouse, a structure which had cast-iron legs to minimise its vulnerability to wave action. It was swept away on 5 February 1850.

James Walker, engineer-in-chief to Trinity House, started construction of a replacement in 1852.[1] It was a circular tower of dove-tailed granite blocks, 35 ft in diameter at the base and about 70 ft high. The work was completed in 1857. Walker's successor, James Douglass, modified the tower in 1881 by encasing it in a granite sleeve, extended upwards to raise the lantern to a height of 143 ft above mean high water. He also strengthened the base with granite blocks bolted to the rock. The work was completed in 1887.

The light has a range of 29 miles. A steel helicopter deck was added in 1977, now a standard provision for all offshore lighthouses.

1. DOUGLASS W. T. The Bishop Rock lighthouses. *Min. Proc. Instn Civ. Engrs*, 1891–92, **108**, 207–220.

2. Wolf Rock Lighthouse

◆

HEW 76

SW 268 120

Wolf Rock is 9 miles south-west of Land's End. It was so named because of the howling sound caused by air escaping from a hollow in the rock into which it had been compressed by wave action. The sound was loud enough to serve as a warning to ships but eventually the hollow was stopped up by local people. Numerous attempts

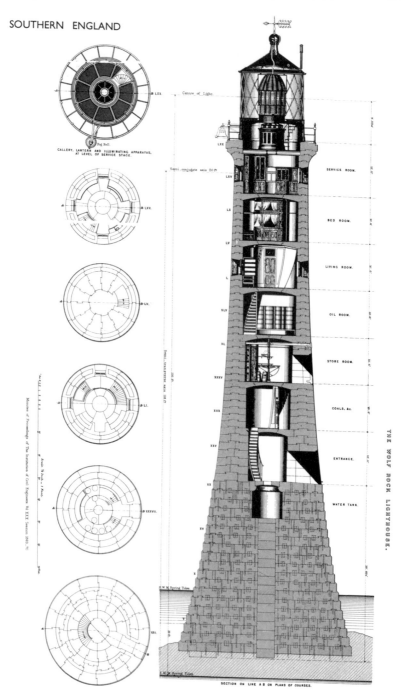

Wolf Rock Lighthouse, 1869, *Min. Proc. Instn Civ. Engrs*, **30**, 1969–70

were made from 1791 onwards to provide a beacon, but few of the results survived for long.

The present light, dating from 1870, was designed by James Walker and built by James Douglass.[1] It is a 135 ft high granite tower; the individual blocks are dove-tailed, bolted and cement grouted. There are seven floors below the lantern.

A feature of the work was the substantial platform or landing stage which had to be built to enable further construction to proceed. The light has a range of 16 miles.

1. DOUGLASS J. N. The Wolf Rock lighthouse. *Min. Proc. Instn Civ. Engrs*, 1869–70, **30**, 1–20.

3. Longships Lighthouse

♦

HEW 1358

SW 320 253

A lighthouse was established on the group of rocks called Carn Bras, 1¼ miles west of Land's End, in 1795. It was founded at a height of 58 ft above high water but 80 years later replacement became necessary because of deterioration of the rock. The Engineer-in-Chief of Trinity House, James Douglass, designed a new lighthouse which was constructed between 1872 and 1875.

The circular grey granite tower was founded 45 ft above high water. It is 86 ft high to the gallery and has a base diameter of 27 ft and a top diameter of 17 ft; the walls are 10 ft thick at the base and 2 ft 6 in. thick at the top. The lantern is 18 ft high and 14 ft in diameter. The light has a range of 16 miles.

4. Smeaton's Pier, St Ives

♣

HEW 1397

SW 521 406

St Ives harbour[1-3] is on the west side of St Ives bay, on the north coast of Cornwall. It is contained by a small pier extending eastwards at the south side and the main, Smeaton's, Pier extending southwards on the eastern side so that the entrance faces south. Smeaton proposed that the pier should be founded on a tipped stone mound 9 ft below low water; this was, in turn, founded on sand proved by probing to be acceptably dense at a depth about 6 ft below the seabed.

The pier was to be 360 ft in length with a top width of 24 ft and a height of 36 ft above the foundations, sur-

Smeaton's Pier, St Ives

mounted by a 9 ft high parapet wall about 15 ft above high water level. On the large random stones of the foundation, the core of the pier was built of rubble masonry retained by external walls of coursed masonry battered at 1 to 2 on each side. At the root of the pier a reservoir was constructed which filled at high tide and emptied at low tide to scour the shallow part of the harbour in the angle between the wharf and the breakwater.

Plan of St Ives Harbour, with the design for the new pier

Construction was between 1767 and 1770. The contractor was Thomas Richardson who had been Smeaton's

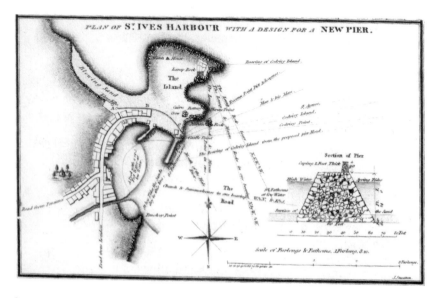

foreman mason on the Eddystone lighthouse (HEW 73, p. 48). The pier was extended 300 ft to its present length in the 1890s.

1. SKEMPTON A. W. (ed.). *John Smeaton FRS*. Thomas Telford, London, 1981, 195 and 198.

2. *Reports of the late John Smeaton FRS*. Longman, London, 1812, I, 295–300.

3. *A catalogue of the designs of the late John Smeaton FRS, preserved in the Royal Society Library*. Newcomen Society, London, 1950, 5, f 167v– 170.

5. Lizard Lighthouse

♦

HEW 1369

SW 705 115

The lighthouse, built in 1752, is sited 1000 yd east of Lizard Point, the most southerly promontory in Britain and has a private approach road.

There are two towers, octagonal in plan, 40 ft high to gallery level, each 13 ft 3 in. wide internally with 3 ft 9 in. thick walls. The west tower is used for storage and the navigation light is exhibited from the east tower at a height of about 190 ft above sea-level. The range is about 21 miles. The lantern was originally fired by coal and subsequently by oil; it was later superseded by a new lantern with an electric light. Drawings of 1873–74 were signed by J. N. Douglass.

6. Early Tram-roads: Poldice-Portreath and Redruth-Chasewater

♠

HEW 1824

Poldice-Portreath:
SW 65 45 to 72 43

Redruth-Chasewater:
SW 70 42 to 80 38

The enormous early nineteenth century development of mining for copper, tin and lead overwhelmed packhorse travel and led to the construction of tram-roads,[1] some of which later formed the basis of railways. Their function was to convey ore from the mines to the ports and conversely to convey coal to the mines for the pumping and winding engines.

One such tram-road started in 1809 and ran from Portreath to Scorrier House. In 1818 it was extended to Poldice. It was worked by horses, had a 4 ft gauge and was in use until about 1865.

Another tram-road became known as the Redruth and

Chasewater Railway. Also of 4 ft gauge, it had wrought iron rails and was opened in 1826 from Wheal Buller to Narabo Quays near Devoran. Later it was extended westwards past Devoran to Point and northwards to Redruth. In 1854, gravity and horse traction was superseded by steam. The annual traffic of 60 000 tons in the 1830s increased to 90 000 tons 30 years later, before trade decreased and a receiver was appointed in 1879. The last train ran in September 1915.

1. FAIRCLOUGH A. *The story of Cornwall's railways.* Tor Mark Press, Truro, 7–10.

♠

HEW 1372

SW 871 499 to 476 306

7. West Cornwall Railway

West Cornwall's first 4 ft 8½ in. (standard) gauge track was opened in 1837–38 by the Hayle Railway, to move copper ore from mines in the Camborne–Redruth area to the ports of Hayle and Portreath.[1] The decision to use rail transport was influenced by the success of the 4 ft gauge horse-hauled Redruth and Chasewater Railway (HEW 1824), which opened in 1826 and moved ore to quays near Devoran on the Fal estuary.

Locomotives were used on the Hayle Railway from the start, except for the inclines at Angarrack (SW 58 38) and at Portreath (SW 65 45) which were equipped with steam winding engines. At Penponds (SW 63 39), a 1 in 22 incline, a counterbalance system was used.

Passengers were carried over the 10 miles between Hayle and Redruth from 1843, by which time locomotives were allowed down the Angarrack incline into Hayle, attached to the rope.

The West Cornwall Railway Act was passed in 1846 with powers to purchase the Hayle Railway and extend it to Truro and Penzance. The gauge was to be 7 ft ¼ in. and I. K. Brunel was appointed Engineer. Scarcity of money prevented any progress until, in 1850, powers were obtained to use the standard gauge, subject to the provision that works should be made wide enough to accommodate the broad gauge. In addition, deviations totalling some 4 miles were authorised, to avoid the Penponds and Angarrack inclines. The line was opened between Penzance and Truro (Higher Town) by August 1852.

Nine timber viaducts were required, of which the highest at 100 ft was at Angarrack (HEW 873) and the longest but lowest at Penzance (HEW 874, SX 482 311). The latter was rebuilt in 1871 and finally replacedby an embankment in 1921.

In 1859, the broad gauge Cornwall Railway (HEW 1371) met the standard gauge West Cornwall at Truro. Because the West Cornwall was not financially able to comply with the obligation to lay a third rail, the railway was leased jointly by the Great Western (GWR), Bristol and Exeter and South Devon Railways, who carried out the work. The first broad gauge through trains reached Penzance in November 1866. The company was finally absorbed by the GWR in 1878.

1. MacDermot E. T. and Clinker C. R. *History of the Great Western Railway. Vol. 2: 1863–1921.* Ian Allan, London, 1964, 156–168.

8. The Great County Adit

This intricate system of adits[1] was developed in the eighteenth century to assist the drainage of the many metal ore

HEW 1086

SW 70 45 to 77 45

SW 70 40 to 77 40

Great County Adit outfall

mines. Eventually it covered 15 sq. miles under an area from St Day, to Redruth in the west, Scorrier in the north, Chacewater in the east and Gwennap in the south. There are now over 30 miles of adits with a cross-section on average 6 ft high and 2 ft 6 in. wide with a fall of about 1 in 250.

Many mines were deeper than the adit system but the lift of water to adit level was appreciably less than to ground level; at Wheal Hope mine the adit was 420 ft below surface.

The outfall at Twelveheads (SW 762 418) was into the river Carnon and placed as low as possible, about 39 ft above high water. In 1873, J. H. Collins recorded a discharge of 1450 cu. ft per minute.[2] The tunnels were extended from time to time until about 1900, after which they began to fall into a state of neglect.

1. BUCKLEY J. A. The great county adit: a model of co-operation. *Journal of the Trevithick Society*. 1989, **16**.

2. COLLINS J. H. The mining districts of Cornwall and west Devon. *Proc. Instn Mech. Engrs*, 1873, 89–118.

9. East Pool Pump, Taylor's Shaft East Pool Whim, Michell's Shaft

♣

East Pool
Pump, Taylor's
Shaft :
HEW 880
SW 674 418

East Pool
Whim,
Michell's Shaft:
HEW 879
SW 672 415

West Cornwall's landscape is punctuated by gaunt ruined buildings which were once mine engine houses.[1] Some of them provided power to drain the mines. It was not usual to raise the water to the surface but only to bring it to the level of an adit which would carry it to a nearby stream. Other smaller engines were the whims used to wind ore or waste rock to the surface.

One of the largest and most recently built was constructed in 1892, by Harvey and Company of Hayle, to pump water from the deep Carn Brea mines. In 1924, following the closure of the mines, the engine was re-erected at its present site at Taylor's shaft, East Pool, and was thus the last Cornish engine to be erected anywhere in the world.

At Taylor's shaft, the engine originally pumped from a depth of 1700 ft. The weight of the total column of water was 85 tons, equal to 27 lb/in^2 of piston area, a heavy load for a Cornish engine which worked at 15 lb/in^2 for maxi-

East Pool,
Taylor's Shaft
Pump

mum efficiency. The cylinder is 90 in. in diameter and the piston stroke is 10 ft. Designed by a local engineer, Nicholas Trestrail, the engine is now the property of the National Trust, as is the whim on a nearby site.

East Pool mine closed in 1945, but the engine was kept working by the South Crofty Mine Company to prevent their own mine from being flooded. The engine, therefore, continued to pump from a lesser depth of 1034 ft until 1954 when it was relieved by electric pumps at South Crofty.

The double acting condensing whim engine has a 30 in. diameter cylinder with the unusually long stroke of 9 ft and works at a steam pressure of 40 lb/in^2. It would do a day's hoisting on a few hundredweight of coal. The engine ran at 17 rpm and because it had no gears was exceedingly quiet. A long I-section connecting rod joined a crank on the flywheel axle near ground level. This, too, was of I-section with eight cruciform spokes and was set between the two winding drums.

Ropes from the winding drums led to the 60 ft head-frame over Michell's shaft, which was 40 yd east of the engine house. The 1300 ft inclined shaft was put out of action in 1920. The plant was allowed to deteriorate but since the Second World War has been gradually restored as a tourist attraction. The engine was originally manufactured in 1877 by Holman Bros of Camborne to the design of a local engineer, F. W. Michell, after whom the shaft was named.

1. LAWS P. *Cornish engines and engine houses.* The National Trust, London, 2nd ed, 1978, 11–25.

10. Falmouth Port

♦

HEW 1895

SW 817 325

Falmouth is situated on the estuary of the River Fal, the finest natural harbour on the south coast. Truro, 9 miles inland, was the main port until Elizabethan times when the increasing size of ships encouraged development of deeper water ports nearer to the sea. These included Penryn (SW 790 342), which has been a port since 1308, and Falmouth. From St Anthony Head (SW 846 310) to the King Harry chain ferry (SW 842 395) the depth of water is over 5 fathoms, adequate for many modern ships. Other historic ports in the estuary include Roundwood Quay (HEW 645, SW 838 404), which dates from 350 BC and handled copper and tin. Remains of the ancient quay may be seen. The port fell into disuse in the nineteenth century and is now National Trust property.

From 1688 to 1852 Falmouth was the packet port for the Royal Mail. Southampton (HEW 1586, p.152) then took over because of the direct rail connection between the port and London. However, Falmouth began to develop as a ship repair centre and a small dockyard, with two dry docks being built following the foundation of the Docks company as the statutory authority in 1859. As the first substantial port in the English Channel reached by homeward bound ships, Falmouth was convenient for ships damaged at sea, especially as the entrance was easy and well protected from south-westerly gales. A demand also arose for passengers to be put ashore for onward travel by Royal Mail stage coach and, after 1863, by rail. To save time, ships transferred passengers to tender which used a masonry wharf close to the town centre.

In 1903 the Prince of Wales, later King George V, inaugurated work on an extension (HEW 1896 SW 807 330) at right angles to the wharf using Hennebique ferro-concrete (reinforced concrete) to the design of L. G. Mouchel. The 5 in. thick reinforced concrete deck is 900 ft long, 36 ft wide, supported at 20 ft 3 in. intervals by trestles of three reinforced concrete piles at around 15 ft centres. These were driven to rock through 8 ft of soft material. To counter lack of stability due to small penetration, the piles were encased in mass concrete, thus forming 2 ft 6 in. diameter columns from deck level to the seabed. This was an early example of the sleeving of reinforced concrete piles. All the bracing is horizontal. The depth alongside is about 7 ft at low water and the distance from deck to sea bed is 30 ft. The extension to the wharf was named the Prince of Wales Pier.

In 1930, No. 1 dock was reconstructed to take 12 000 ton ships and between 1955 and 1958 the Queen Elizabeth dock[1] was built for 90 000 ton tankers, but was too small to accommodate the super tankers which developed a few years later.

1. UNDERWOOD A. E. *et al*. The design and construction of the Queen Elizabeth Graving Dock at Falmouth. *Proc. Instn Civ. Engrs*, 1960, **15**, Jan., 49–64.

11. Cornwall Railway

With the opening of the South Devon Railway (SDR) to Plymouth in 1848 (HEW 1353, p.68) and the West Cornwall Railway (HEW 1372) from Truro to Penzance in

HEW 1371
SX 473 553 to
SW 817 449
and SW 811
320

1852, only the length from Plymouth to Truro prevented the completion of the route from London to Penzance.

An act of 1846 had authorised a two-track broad gauge railway from Plymouth to Falmouth[1] and I. K. Brunel was appointed Engineer. However, because of financial difficulties, work did not proceed effectively until 1852, when the Board of Trade agreed to a mainly single line track. The overbridges and tunnels were to be built for double lines.

Work proceeded slowly, the terrain being difficult and necessitating steep gradients and sharp curves; additionally, Brunel needed numerous viaducts, mainly of timber (HEW 873 etc.). However, the most notable structure was the Royal Albert Bridge (HEW 29, p.41) over the River Tamar. The line was opened between Plymouth and Truro in 1859 and on to Falmouth in 1863.

The railway was leased to the Great Western, (GWR), the Bristol and Exeter and the West Cornwall Railways from 1861 and finally acquired by the GWR in 1889. By this time the GWR had converted virtually all its lines east of Exeter to standard or mixed gauge. In May 1892 came the final conversion to standard gauge covering the lines of the SDR and the Cornwall Railway. On double track it was possible to carry out the conversion in two stages, by taking one track out of action first, with single line working on the other. This applied to about three quarters of the South Devon main line, along with its branch from Newton Abbot to Torquay, which had single line working from 2 to 20 May. The brunt of the work fell on the Cornwall Railway, which was single line. The whole conversion was successfully carried out over the weekend of 20– 23 May 1892. Where there was already mixed gauge, the third rail was removed at leisure.

After the gauge conversion, the main line was doubled in stages between Saltash and Truro and this process was completed in 1908 by the construction of a deviation of the line between Wearde Quay, near Saltash, and St Germans.

1. WOODFIN R. J. *The centenary of the Cornwall railway.* Jefferson, Ely, 1960.

12. Timber railway viaducts in Cornwall: Angarrack, Collegewood, St Pinnock, Moorswater

♦
(Demolished)

Angarrack:
HEW 873
SW 585 381

Collegewood:
HEW 878
SW 781 343

St Pinnock:
HEW 877
SX 178 646

Moorswater:
HEW 654

Occasionally at the sites of Cornwall's masonry arched railway viaducts a series of masonry piers can be seen on a parallel alignment. These are all that remain as reminders that originally all the major structures of both the West Cornwall (HEW 1372) and Cornwall Railways (HEW 1371), except the Royal Albert Bridge, were built using timber superstructures. On the West Cornwall Railway, Brunel built nine timber viaducts on the 26 mile route. On the Cornwall Railway there were 34 timber viaducts on the 52 miles from Plymouth to Truro (the viaducts carried 4 miles of track) and between Truro and Falmouth there were eight viaducts. They ranged in size from 12 to 151 ft high and 114 to 1329 ft long.

In some respects the choice of timber as the structural material for the viaducts had been determined by the lack of capital available to the companies but there is nothing to suggest that Brunel considered the timber viaducts to be of a temporary nature. He used yellow pine, which was superior to other pines, Oregon pine giving a life of about 8 years in comparison with an average life of 30 years and even up to 60 years for yellow pine. Brunel paid special attention in design to the problem of replacement of decayed members even though the timber was kyanised (treated with a solution of mercuric chloride).[1]

Commonly, the single track viaducts supported the rails by transverse 12 in. by 6 in. timbers placed side by side, in turn supported by three longitudinal laminated timbers, often of twin 12 in. by 12 in. sections, one central and one each under the parapets. These three longitudinal timbers were then supported in different ways according to the depth of the valley to be crossed.

The aim was to support the longitudinal laminated timbers at about 16–20 ft centres, so for viaducts up to about 50 ft high it was sufficient to place masonry foundations at 40 ft centres and from these to erect two raking sets of three legs giving a V-form in elevation.

When three sets of raking legs were used, as on the Angarrack Viaduct, the span could be increased to 50 ft.

17

The raking legs, which now sprang from a level 41 ft below the deck were supported on vertical timber legs which rested on masonry foundations. For stability a continuous longitudinal timber member was placed at the level of the tops of the vertical legs at the spring point of the raking legs and iron diagonal braces were placed between some of the vertical legs.

For the tallest viaducts, masonry piers at 60–66 ft centres were brought to 35 ft below deck level. This time, the three longitudinal beams were each supported by four raking legs springing from cast-iron shoes on the tops of the masonry piers. With the legs raking at 80° or 60° to the horizontal and transversely braced with horizontal and diagonal members, each bay was stiffened by metal ties which ran horizontally and diagonally from the pier heads. St Pinnock and Moorswater viaducts were built in this way.

Replacement of the viaducts started in 1871[2] when an embankment was substituted for Probus Viaduct. The process continued on the main line between Plymouth and Penzance for the next 37 years. Most of the timber viaducts were replaced by masonry arches but on four bridges on straight track, wrought iron and later steel spans were erected on upward extensions of the original piers. Examples of these methods are described in Margary's paper on the reconstruction of St Pinnock and Moorswater Viaducts.[3] All these conversions were designed to take two tracks. However, on the Truro–Falmouth line, where single track remains, the conversions followed later. After 1923 four viaducts were replaced by brick-faced concrete arch structures and four others by embankments. Collegewood Viaduct was the last to be reconstructed in 1934 after a life of 71 years.

1. Pugsley Sir A. (ed.). *The works of Isambard Kingdom Brunel: an engineering appreciation*. Institution of Civil Engineers and University of Bristol, London and Bristol, 1976,134.

2. Woodfin R. J. *The centenary of the Cornwall Railway*. Jefferson, Ely, 1960, 45–58.

3. Margary P. J. Reconstruction of St Pinnock and Moorswater Viaducts on the Cornwall Railway. *Min. Proc. Instn Civ. Engrs*, 1882, **69**, 312–317.

Opposite: Wheal Martyn Water-wheel, St Austell

13. Wheal Martyn Water-wheel, St Austell

♣

HEW 795

SX 005 554

Before the industrial revolution, the main source of power was water, but in the mines and clay pits of Cornwall power was often required at points where it

was inconvenient to bring the water. One solution was to transmit power by the use of horizontal iron rods supported at intervals on rollers and reciprocated by a crank on the water-wheel. Bell cranks enabled the direction to be changed so that plunger pumps in pit shafts could be so driven.

An excellent example may be seen at the Wheal Martyn China Clay Museum.[1] The wheel, which is 35 ft in diameter and of the overshot pitch back type, operated a series of rods for a distance of 1000 yd to plunger pumps in a shaft halfway down the side of Wheal Martyn pit. The horizontal rods traversed the pan kiln and settling tank areas and passed through a granite lined tunnel in a hillside before turning vertically at the pit. This installation pumped china clay slurry to the surface level.

The name 'Charlestown' is cast in the rim of the wheel. The date of installation is unknown but a map dated 1884 shows a wheel at the site. Following the closure of Wheal Martyn pit in 1930 the wheel continued to be used to keep the pit dewatered until 1940. Subsequently it was restored and turned again in 1976.

1. *Wheal Martyn Museum.* St Austell Clay Museum Ltd, 1983, 5th edn.

♣ 14. Charlestown Harbour

HEW 139

SX 039 517

Charlestown, near St Austell, is a delightful example of a small harbour in active use, much as it was over a century ago.[1]

Charles Rashleigh promoted this industrial area and probably instructed John Smeaton to design the harbour that he needed for supplies to the mines and for exporting ore. Construction began in 1791 and took nine years. Smeaton died in 1792. The buildings date from the same time. There is an outer basin protected by a breakwater constructed in coursed and random granite masonry and a small spending beach. Ships up to 170 ft long can be accommodated. Few alterations or additions have been made except for the replacement of the mitre gates to the non-tidal inner basin by a rising gate that lies on the invert of the entrance when open. This increased the width of the entrance from 28 ft to 35 ft and enabled ships with a maximum draught of 12 ft to enter the dock.

The export of copper ore continued until the mid-nine-teenth century and then gave way to china clay. This trade also has very much diminished in recent years.

1. GILBERT C. S. *An historical survey of Cornwall 1817–20.* **2**, 867.

15. Treffry Viaduct

♣

This was the first large granite viaduct built in Cornwall and is now a Scheduled Ancient Monument. It was completed in 1842 as part of a local industrial transport system devised by Joseph T. Treffry to carry china clay from workings north of St Austell to the port of Par. The system comprised a mile of canal from Par to Ponts Mill (SX 073 563), followed by a standard gauge waggon track to Bugle (Molinnis) (SX 020 593). The railway ascended a 1 in 10 incline at Carmears and crossed the Luxulyan valley on the viaduct. Horse traction was used except on the incline where empty waggons were hauled up by water power.

The granite viaduct,[1] designed by William Pease, is 650 ft long and of 98 ft maximum height. It comprises ten

HEW 567

SX 056 571

Treffry Viaduct

arches of 40 ft span, the arch rings being of the stepped voussoir type with projecting keystones. A granite slab supported the railway and beneath the deck an aqueduct carried the water supply to operate the water-wheel at the incline.

1. WOODFIN R. J. *The centenary of the Cornwall Railway*. Jefferson, Ely, 1960, 9.

THOMAS D. St J. *West Country railway history*. David and Charles, Newton Abbot, 1973, 149.

♣

HEW 1602

SX 106 598

16. Lostwithiel Bridge

The lowest crossing of the River Fowey is at Lostwithiel, by a bridge carrying a former route of the Liskeard to St Austell road through the town centre.

The western five pointed arches are thought to date from 1437, when Bishop Lacy of Exeter granted an Indulgence for its repair.[1] They have double rings with thin slate voussoirs and vary in span from 11 ft to 12 ft 6 in.

The two most easterly arches, of 10 ft 3 in. span, which are separated from the remainder by an island, were rebuilt in the eighteenth century. They replaced a timber bridge, which had been built some 200 years earlier when a new channel had been dug which formed the island. The two remaining arches, situated between the island and the oldest portion of the bridge, are of 6 ft 3 in. and 14 ft 3 in. span and may have been added at the same time as the east spans were rebuilt.

Lostwithiel Bridge

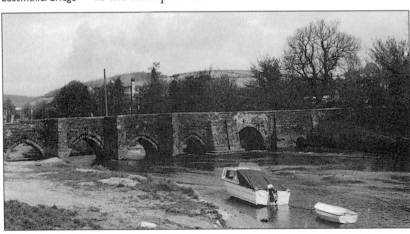

The width between parapets varies from 11 ft 6 in. to 14 ft 9 in. There is no footway, but the cutwaters continue upwards to form refuges. The bridge is a Scheduled Ancient Monument.

1. HENDERSON C. and COATES H. *Old Cornish bridges.* Simpkin Marshall, London, 1928, 77–79. Reprinted Bradford Barton, Truro, 1972.

17. Bodmin and Wadebridge Railway ♠

HEW 1367

SW 991 722 to
SX 086 751

In 1831 Sir William Molesworth, a landowner, engaged the Plymouth civil engineer, Roger Hopkins, to survey a railway route from Wadebridge to Wenfordbridge with branches to Bodmin and Ruthernbridge. The Bodmin and Wadebridge line was Cornwall's first standard gauge railway and also the first with steam traction. It was opened from Wadebridge to Bodmin and to Wenfordbridge in 1834.

The purpose was to carry ore and granite from the de Lank quarries to Wadebridge for shipment and to convey inland limestone shelly sea sand as fertiliser for agricultural use; the latter became the main traffic. In 1862, china clay traffic from the dries at Wenfordbridge started and continued until the closure of the line in 1983. Passenger services ran on the Wadebridge to Bodmin section only and closed in 1967.

The steepest gradient was 1 in 51 for nearly 2 miles between Dunmere junction and Bodmin. There were eight bridges over the river Camel and other streams, including an 18 ft span bascule bridge. Originally the track was 42 lb/yd; rails were set on granite blocks 20 in.^{2} by 12 in. deep.

The line was acquired by the London and South Western Railway(LSWR)[1] in 1846 but it was not until 1895 that the North Cornwall Railway linked it with Launceston and the LSWR system. In 1888, the Great Western Railway laid a branch line from Bodmin Road station on the Cornwall Railway (HEW 1371) to Bodmin and thence to Boscarne junction. Two Bodmin and Wadebridge vehicles are preserved at the National Railway Museum, York.

1. WILLIAMS R. A. *The London and South Western Railway. Vol. 1.* David and Charles, Newton Abbot, 1973, 101–106, plates 7 to 14.

♣

18. Wadebridge Ancient Bridge

HEW 882

SW 991 724

Above:
Wadebridge
Ancient Bridge

Although the bridge originally comprised 17 pointed arches including two smaller spans at each end, only 13 of the 19 ft span arches can be seen today. The overall length of the bridge is about 400 ft. It was built on the site of an old ford which was considered dangerous. John Lovebond, vicar of the nearby parish of Egloshayle, began the bridge with John de Harlyn as Contractor in 1460. It was mentioned in William of Worcester's itinerary of 1478 and was reported by Leland in 1538.[1]

The old bridge was 9 ft wide, but in 1853 it was widened under the direction of William Pease, Surveyor of Bridges for the eastern division of Cornwall. Segmental arches 3 ft wide were sprung from the existing cutwaters.

In 1962, with the bridge carrying the A39 Trunk Road, a further widening of 21 ft was carried out on behalf of the Ministry of Transport to the design of Posford, Pavry and Partners. This consisted of precast reinforced concrete ribs with piers and spandrel wall masonry faced to Ancient Monument standards and supported on 24 in. diameter bored piles, six per pier.

The bridge at road level is now 36 ft wide and although the old pointed arches remain they can only be seen from the river; the upstream elevation dates from 1962 and the downstream side is as modified by the Victorian widening.

1. HENDERSON C. and COATES H. *Old Cornish bridges*. Simpkin Marshall, London, 1928, 115–119. Reprinted Bradford Barton, Truro, 1972.

19. Treverbyn Bridge

♣

On 21 January, in either 1412 or 1413, Bishop Stafford granted an Indulgence in favour of the bridge of Treverbyn, spanning the River Fowey between Leskyret and Bodmin and whose condition was described as 'threatening total ruin'.[1] As a result of this Indulgence two arches were evidently built which bear a close resemblance to the arches of Staverton bridge (HEW 1601, p.62) near Totnes, for which an Indulgence was granted at the same time. To the west is an approach span of 8 ft 9 in. which is probably a survival of the older bridge.

With two main spans of 24 ft and a width of 8 ft 6 in. between parapets this bridge was used as part of the main route from Bodmin to Liskeard through St Neot for many hundreds of years. Immediately downstream of the ancient bridge, what is now a local road has been realigned over a single arch reinforced concrete bridge with a 22 ft carriageway and footways. This was built in 1929 by E. H. Collcutt AMICE, County Surveyor of Cornwall.

HEW 1563

SX 206 675

Above:
Treverbyn Bridge

1. HENDERSON C. and COATES H. *Old Cornish bridges*. Simpkin Marshall, London, 1928, 71–72. Reprinted Bradfield Barton, Truro, 1972.

SOUTHERN ENGLAND

SS

Bude

DEVON

R. Ottery

R. Tamar

Okehampton

Launceston

R. Inny

CORNWALL

Tavistock

R. Tavy Canal

R. Walkham

Liskeard

Lostwithiel

Looe

Plymouth

Scale in km
0   10

0   5
Scale in miles

1. Bude Canal and Sea Lock
2. The Tamar Dams
3. Trekelland and Yeolm Bridges
4. Tamar Ancient Bridges
5. Morwellham Port, Tavistock Canal
6. Calstock Viaduct
7. Horrabridge Ancient Bridge
8. Walkham Viaduct
9. Drake's and Devonport Leats
10. Burrator and Sheepstor Dams
11. Tamar Suspension Bridge
12. Royal Albert Bridge
13. Torpoint Chain Ferry
14. Devonport South Yard
15. Royal William Victualling Yard
16. Chelson Meadow
17. Plymouth Breakwater
18. Eddystone Lighthouse (Smeaton)
19. Eddystone Lighthouse (Douglass)

26

2. The Tamar Valley and Plymouth

T he River Tamar, which very nearly crosses the West Country peninsula, forms the boundary between Devon and Cornwall. At its north end,
about 6 miles from the coast of Bude Bay, are the Tamar Dams; the first of
these was built to provide a reservoir for the Bude canal which ran almost
to Launceston. To the south, the river's tidal reach extended into a mining
area with the port of Morwellham lying at the bottom of two inclined
planes, one from the Devon Great Consols mine and the other from the
southern end of the Tavistock canal. Whereas the river, therefore, has
made a contribution to the movement of ore and other goods, together
with its tributaries it has been a major physical barrier to both roads and
railways.

A number of medieval masonry bridges survive, like those at Trekelland over the River Inny, Yeolm over the River Ottery and a series of
bridges at Greystone, Horsebridge and Gunnislake within a 6 mile reach
of the Tamar. The most impressive structures, however, cross the estuary
at Saltash. Brunel's Royal Albert Bridge, one of the nation's most famous,
conveys the railway into Cornwall and the immediately adjacent, but
much more recent, Tamar Suspension Bridge carries the A38 trunk road,
which joins the M5 motorway at Exeter. A short way further down the
estuary a chain ferry, originally designed by James Rendel, conveys traffic
between Torpoint and Devonport.

Devonport's naval dockyard has numerous examples of early dock and
harbour engineering, including the nation's oldest covered slipway,
whereas the associated Royal William Victualling Yard contains a substantial group of industrial buildings dating from the 1830s. Sir Francis
Drake, more famous for his maritime than for his engineering exploits,
was involved in the provision of a water supply to Plymouth from
Dartmoor in the late 1500s. A similar scheme provided Devonport's
supply in 1793 and a century later a mass concrete gravity dam impounded a reservoir at Burrator to ensure adequate supplies.

The relatively sheltered waters of Plymouth Sound are given further
protection by Rennie's massive offshore breakwater which permitted

Plymouth's development as an important naval base to continue during the nineteenth century. On a fine day, the Eddystone Lighthouse can be seen standing 10 miles offshore. Smeaton's famous structure, built in the 1750s, has been re-erected on Plymouth Hoe.

A number of the area's engineering features, including canal, bridge and roadworks and the Chelson Meadow reclamation are attributable to James Green, who was one of Rennie's assistants between 1800 and 1808 and was Devon's County Surveyor for 33 years. Further examples of his work are described in section 3.

Bude Canal and
Sea-Lock

1. Bude Canal and Sea Lock

The Bude Sea Lock and Wharf plus the 2 miles of barge canal from thence to Helebridge, below the village of Marhamchurch, are the main remaining items of the Bude Canal.[1] It extended east to Holsworthy and south to Launceston and was 35 miles in total length. It was constructed by James Green in 1823, to provide three branches of tub-boat canal, principally to enable limestone sea sand to be carried inland for soil improvement.

Bude Canal:
HEW 1065
SS 204 064 to
215 034

Bude Sea Lock:
HEW 1066
SS 204 064

In the hilly countryside above Marhamchurch, Green provided a tub-boat canal for modest loads with one horse towing four 20 ft long, 4 ton boats. The canal was 10 ft wide at the bottom, 3 ft deep and 19 ft wide at water level. Instead of lock staircases, six twin track inclined planes were built. This meant that the boats required wheels, which unfortunately damaged the canal banks. The site of the first inclined plane, 120 ft rise and 836 ft long, can be seen between Marhamchurch village and Helebridge, adjacent to the A39 trunk road. The canal remained in use until 1891, supplied with water retained by the Tamar Lake Dam (HEW 1488).

The sea lock was enlarged in 1835 by James Meadows Rendel to be 116 ft long and 29 ft 6 in. wide in order to admit 300 ton ships to the wharf. A stone and rubble breakwater was also built to protect the lock approach. This is still in use, as the wharf provides winter berths for many local vessels.

1. Harris H. and Ellis M. *The Bude Canal*. David and Charles, Newton Abbot, 1972, 142–164.

2. The Tamar Dams: Lower Dam and Upper Dam

There are two reservoirs on the upper reaches of the River Tamar, about 2 miles downstream of the point where the river becomes the boundary between Cornwall and Devon.

HEW 1488

Lower Dam
SS 295 107

Upper Dam
SS 290 117

The lower and older earth dam was constructed in 1820 by James Green to provide a feeder reservoir for the Bude Canal (HEW 1065). It is 180 yd long at the crest and 26 ft high and appears to be the first dam south of Derby-

Lower Tamar
Dam

shire more than 20 ft high. The catchment of 4200 acres supplied a reservoir of 52 acres with storage of 40 million gallons at a top water level of 441 ft above sea-level.

The canal was closed by an Act of Parliament of 1891 but the reservoir was subsequently brought into service to supply piped water via the Venn treatment works (SS 287 065) to the Bude area. It continued in this role until 1978, when a new treatment works, fed from the Upper Lake, became operational.

An upper concrete dam of crest level 490 ft above sea-level was designed by Rofe, Kennard and Lapworth, built by W. and C. French (Construction) Ltd and substantially completed in 1975 to hold 300 million gallons of water. It can supply 1 670 000 gallons per day to the coastal strip from Crackington Haven to Hartland. The new treatment works are close to the lower dam, which is now maintained to provide an area for countryside recreation and wildlife conservation.

3. Trekelland Bridge and Yeolm Bridge

♣

Trekelland
Bridge:
HEW 275
SX 300 798

Trekelland Bridge[1] carries the B3254 Launceston to Liskeard Road over the River Inny. There are two main arches of 19 ft span and a floodwater arch of 8 ft 9 in. span. The carriageway is 10 ft wide.

Yeolm Bridge

The main structure is of dressed granite and the pointed arch soffits are four-centred Elizabethan style. The parapets, with refuges over the cutwaters, are of random delabole slate, probably repairs to the original construction.

Yeolm Bridge:
HEW 1903
SX 318 874

There is no record of the bridge's construction but it is thought to date from around 1500. The bridge is well proportioned and is one of the best preserved of the many ancient Cornish bridges.

Approximately 2 miles north of Launceston, the B3254 is carried over the River Ottery by Yeolm Bridge.[2] Thought to be the oldest and most perfectly finished ancient Cornish bridge dating from around 1350, it has also been described as Cornwall's 'most ambitious.'[3] Its medieval form can be viewed from upstream with a cutwater and refuge to its centre pier. The two pointed arches, of 18 ft 3 in. span, are built of dressed stone with parapets, clearly rebuilt, of random rubble with stone on edge copings. The original 11 ft 6 in. roadway was widened in 1877. The bridge is a Scheduled Ancient Monument and is Listed Grade I.

1. HENDERSON C. and COATES H. *Old Cornish bridges*. Simpkin Marshall, London, 1928, 57–58. Reprinted Bradford Barton, Truro, 1972.

2. Ibid., 28 and 43.

3. PEVSNER N. *The buildings of England — Cornwall*. Penguin, Harmondsworth, 1951, 220.

4. Ancient Bridges over the River Tamar: Greystone, Horse Bridge and Gunnislake, New Bridge

♣

Greystone:
HEW 273
SX 368 803

Horse Bridge:
HEW 1544
SX 400 748

New Bridge:
HEW 274
SX 434 723

The River Tamar has three fine ancient bridges[1] within a direct distance of 6 miles. The highest upstream is at Greystone, carrying the Tavistock to Launceston road, and dates from an indulgence granted by Bishop Lacy in 1439. Next downstream is Horse Bridge, also granted an indulgence, in 1437. It now carries a minor road.

Greystone and Horse Bridge appear to be the work of one builder. Greystone has six semicircular arches of 23 ft span and two 14 ft flood arches. The road width is only 10 ft, but cutwaters extend 27 ft from the river bed to parapet level, providing safety recesses for pedestrians.

Horse Bridge has six two-order semicircular main arches of 20 ft span and one flood arch of 15 ft 6 in. span. The height of the central piers from the river bed to parapet level is 30 ft. Like Greystone, the bridge is built of local stone, with freestone dressings. The road width is 12 ft.

Gunnislake, New Bridge dates from about 1520 and carries the Tavistock to Liskeard road. It was the lowest

Horsebridge

downstream road bridge until the opening of the Tamar Suspension Bridge (HEW 202) in 1961.

New Bridge is of dressed granite masonry, and has four slightly pointed arches of 21 ft span, one of 18 ft and one of 14 ft span, springing from a level of 13 ft above water level. The pier cutwaters are taken up to parapet level, 42 ft above the river bed, to provide pedestrian refuges. The road width is 12 ft and the bridge lies just ½ mile above the tidal limit.

The survival of all three bridges in good condition over 500 years across this powerful river is attributable to careful construction in firm foundations, an adequate number of arches providing clearance for river debris and the careful building of the piers, particularly their heartings. Modern traffic is only moderate. The three bridges are Scheduled Ancient Monuments.

1. HENDERSON C. and COATES H. *Old Cornish bridges*. Simpkin Marshall, London, 1928, 49–53. Reprinted Bradford Barton, Truro, 1972.

5. Morwellham, River Port and Tavistock Canal

Morwellham is on the River Tamar about 20 miles above Plymouth and was a port for Tavistock in 1105 when the town was granted a weekly market. In the nineteenth century the quay owed its importance to the opening of the Tavistock Canal in 1817, which halved the cost of carriage from Tavistock, and also to the opening of the Devon Great Consols mine at Blanchdown, 1 mile north-east of Gunnislake in 1844.[1] Adjacent to the quay was the George and Charlotte copper mine.

Copper ore on the Tavistock canal was transported via a 2540 yd long tunnel, built by John Taylor, running 360 ft under Morwell Down. It is 12 ft from the roof to the invert and 6 ft wide. The hill contained slate and hard elvan rock that delayed completion and added £20 000 to the estimated cost of £40 000. Tunnelling started on 27 August 1803, as shown on the portals, but was not through until August 1816 and the tunnel opened to traffic on 24 June 1817. Not far from the northern portal, three areas of copper ore were found, which were developed as Wheal Crebor, but otherwise the drive through the Down was

Morwellham,
River Port:
HEW 1082
SX 446 697

Tavistock
Canal:
HEW 668
SX 448 703 to
462 723

Tavistock Canal

poorly rewarded for an area that seemed to abound in minerals.

Material from the canal and from Blanchdown descended from the 250 ft and 400 ft contours respectively by adjacent inclined railways. New quays were built for 300 ton vessels in 1858 and Morwellham was one of the most important copper exporting centres in Europe. However, the advent of the railway from Plymouth to Tavistock in 1859 took trade from the Tavistock canal and its incline was broken up in 1888. The Great Consols mine soon closed and by 1896 the quays were deserted.

Since 1933 the canal has powered two Pelton wheel-driven alternators delivering 640 kW to the national grid. The port has been developed since 1970 as an open air museum by a charitable body under the auspices of the Dartington Hall Trust and there are numerous relics to be seen. The raised railways in the dock area are being restored but were badly damaged by floods in December 1979. Water power is also represented by a 32 ft diameter overshot wheel which typifies one used to grind manganese from the Brentor–Milton Abbot district.

1. BOOKER F. *Industrial archaeology of the Tamar valley*. David and Charles, Newton Abbot, 1967, 27–35, 103–127.

6. Calstock Viaduct

♣

This viaduct[1] over the River Tamar carried a branch line from Gunnislake to join the London and South Western Railway's Exeter to Plymouth route at Bere Alston. It was designed by W. R. Galbraith and R. Church using precast concrete block construction and was built between 1904 and 1907. There are 12 semicircular arches of 60 ft span, the soffits of which are 108 ft above ground level. Below ground, in-situ concrete foundations are taken to a maximum depth of 47 ft to the sandstone surface.

HEW 595

SX 433 686

The width of the viaduct is 14 ft 6 in. between parapets and the piers, which are 17 ft 6 in. by 7 ft 6 in. at the top, taper at 1 to 24 from the larger dimension and at 1 to 48 from the lesser dimension outwards and downwards to the bases, which measure 35 ft by 16 ft. The arch rings are 3 ft thick and large blocks, of the order of 5 ft by 3 ft by 2 ft, were used for the voussoirs, piers and spandrels. The contractor was John Charles Lang and the viaduct is listed as a building of historical interest.

1. BURGE J. T. The reconstructed East Cornwall Railway. *Railway Magazine*, 1908, **22**, Feb., 102–108.

Calstock Viaduct

♣

7. Horrabridge, Ancient Bridge

HEW 1621

SX 513 699

Above:
Horrabridge

In 1396 an indulgence was granted by Bishop Stafford of Exeter for the construction of this bridge[1] to carry the original Okehampton to Plymouth road over the River Walkham, 4 miles south-east of Tavistock. It was still on the main road and called Harrowbridge in the Ordnance Survey of 1809, but now is located on a side road and gives its name to the surrounding village of Horrabridge.

Two of the three arches are 14 ft span and the other is 11 ft. All three arches have two pointed rings and spring from about 6 ft above low water with a rise of 6 ft. Piers are about 6 ft wide at the base and pointed cutwaters extend upwards to the parapets to form recesses for pedestrians. The road width is 11 ft 6 in. The bridge is Listed Grade II and is a Scheduled Ancient Monument.

1. HENDERSON C. and JERVOISE E. *Old Devon bridges*. Wheaton, Exeter, 1938, 17–18.

8. Walkham Viaduct

♦
(demolished)

A single line broad gauge branch of the South Devon
Railway (HEW 1353, p.68) was opened to Tavistock from
the Exeter to Plymouth main line at Marsh Mills, Plympton on 22 June 1859. Thirteen miles long, the engineering
works included three tunnels and six timber viaducts.
The largest viaduct, 1101 ft long and 132 ft high, was over
the River Walkham,[1] which flows off the west side of
Dartmoor to join the River Tavy.

HEW 877

SX 495 705

Three sets of four raking legs sprang at angles of 60°
and 80° in side elevation from the tops of masonry piers,
35 ft below deck level, to support three sets of longitudinal timbers carrying the deck. Each bay was stiffened
with wrought iron ties which ran horizontally and diagonally from the pier heads. With piers set at 60–66 ft
centres, no horizontal load carrying beam spanned more
than 16 ft.

In 1910, Walkham was the last viaduct to be replaced
by masonry arches on this route. It was considered by
some to be the most mature of Brunel's timber fan designs.[2] The branch was closed to passengers in 1962 and
the track has since been lifted.

1. PUGSLEY SIR A. (ed.). *The works of Isambard Kingdom Brunel: an engineering appreciation.* Institution of Civil Engineers and University of
Bristol, London and Bristol, 1976, 126.

2. MACDERMOT E. T. and CLINKER C. R. *History of the Great Western
Railway. Vol. 2: 1863–1921.* Ian Allan, London, 1964, 124.

9. Drake's Leat and Devonport Leat

♠

In 1584 Sir Francis Drake was a member of a Parliamentary committee which approved a Bill for bringing water
from the River Meavy to Plymouth as the town's first
public supply. The leat was 17 miles long, about 6 ft wide
and 2 ft deep and was constructed between December
1590 and April 1591. A century or so later, it was provided with a solid invert and granite sides. It ran from the
River Meavy to the west around Yennadon, then via
Yelverton to Roborough Down and thence to Plymouth.
It is still clearly traceable on Roborough Down (SX 518
651), in Yelverton and near the source.

Drake's Leat:
HEW 1039
SX 550 676 to
483 543

Devonport
Leat :
HEW 1053
SX 608 780 to
553 690

Although Drake's leat had brought water to Ply-

Devonport Leat

mouth, the expansion of Plymouth Dock and Stoke Town, now known as Devonport, required another source further within Dartmoor. Powers for this second leat were obtained by the proprietors of the Plymouth Dock Waterworks in 1793. The leat takes water from the River West Dart (SX 608 779), the Cowsic (SX 595 767) and the Blackbrook (SX 548 766) in the area north of Princetown and passes east of the town winding its way south around the contours to its destination.

The leat has a number of small aqueducts and flows through a 648 yd tunnel near Nun's Cross (SX 605 698). It forms a waterfall as it descends the western slopes of Raddick Hill into the valley of the River Meavy, which it crosses by an aqueduct. Formerly the leat continued from here to Dousland, through Yelverton and over Roborough Down close to the route of Drake's leat proceeding to Crownhill and Devonport. Both leats[1] were clearly shown on the 1809 Ordnance Survey one inch map, marked as the Plymouth leat and the Dock leat.

In 1898, Burrator Reservoir (HEW 549) was completed at the site of the intake to Drake's leat and from then onwards a piped supply from the reservoir made both leats redundant south of Burrator. The Devonport leat is channelled to join the impounded water, thus continuing to augment the supply.

1. HARRIS H. *The industrial archaeology of Dartmoor*. David and Charles, Newton Abbot, 1968, 136–137.

10. Burrator and Sheepstor Dams ♣

These dams[1] impound the Burrator Reservoir, some 8 miles north-east of Plymouth. Built by Plymouth Corporation under an Act of 1893, the reservoir is now the principal source of water for the city. The works, begun in 1893 and completed in 1898, superseded Sir Francis Drake's water supply for Plymouth (HEW 1039).

HEW 549

SX 551 680

The Burrator Dam, across the Meavy, is 361 ft long, 18 ft wide at the crest and 62 ft wide at river bed level. Originally 77 ft high, its crest was raised by 10 ft in 1928, which increased the reservoir's 657 million gallon capacity. It is constructed of concrete containing a high proportion of granite stones from the foundation trench which went down 53 ft. Both sides are faced with granite masonry. Great care was taken to remove all fissures and loose material in the excavation, this being done by hand labour to avoid shock to the underlying ground by blasting. The stones in the dam's body were roughly dressed with flat beds before being carefully set in the concrete.

The Sheepstor Dam closes the gap between the Sheepstor and Burrator hills. It is an earth embankment 470 ft long, with concrete slabs on the water face and grass on the downstream side. Although only 23 ft high, the 5 ft wide concrete cut-off wall had to be taken down 105 ft to reach solid rock. Edward Sandeman, Water Engineer to Plymouth Corporation, designed the dams and supervised their construction by direct labour.

1. SANDEMAN E. The Burrator works for the water supply of Plymouth. *Min. Proc. Instn Civ. Engnrs*, 1901, **146**, 2–24.

11. The Tamar Suspension Bridge, Saltash ♣

Heavy commuting and longer distance traffic across the Tamar Estuary ferries in the 1950s led Cornwall County Council and Plymouth City Council to promote a Tamar bridge crossing.[1] The councils' Consulting Engineers, Mott, Hay and Anderson, proposed a suspension bridge at Saltash, where topography minimised the length of the approaches. It was 200 ft upstream of Brunel's Royal Albert railway bridge (HEW 29).

HEW 202

SX 435 588

Tamar Suspension Bridge , Royal Albert Bridge to left

The suspension bridge is of total length 2107 ft, including abutments, and has a central span of 1100 ft and side spans of 374 ft. The reinforced concrete towers at 50 ft centres rise to 260 ft above sea-level. They are founded on 30 ft diameter caissons sunk to rock. Side towers of a similar type are provided and the anchorages are tunnelled in natural rock on each side of the river. The main suspension comprises a series of locked coil-wire ropes to which are attached similar suspenders at 50 ft centres. These in turn support an 18 ft deep stiffened Warren truss which carries the roadway.

The reinforced concrete bridge deck carries the A38 Exeter–Plymouth–Bodmin trunk road and provides for a 33 ft wide carriageway and two 6 ft wide footways. The Contractors were the Cleveland Bridge and Engineering Company and the bridge was opened to traffic on 24 October 1961. It is a traditional suspension bridge design with trussed stiffening girders, contrasting with the streamlined box girder deck used on the Severn Bridge (HEW 201)[2] built five years later.

1. ANDERSON J. K. Tamar Bridge. *Proc. Instn Civ. Engrs*, 1965, **31**, 337–360.

2. SIVEWRIGHT W. J.(ed.). *Civil engineering heritage: Wales and western England*. Thomas Telford, London, 1986, 85–86.

12. Royal Albert Bridge, Saltash   ♣

HEW 29

SX 435 587

In 1845, the Cornwall Railway Company (HEW 1371, p.15) applied for an Act to extend the South Devon Railway (HEW 1353 p68) from Plymouth to Falmouth , which involved crossing the tidal River Tamar. Their engineer, I. K. Brunel, chose a bridge site 3 miles north-west of Plymouth where the river narrows to 1000 ft.[1] By 1847, an extensive borehole survey of the river bed showed that over the eastern half, solid rock was over-lain by a layer of mud up to 16 ft thick but over the western half the rock fell away to much greater depths. Brunel, therefore, decided to build a bridge of two main 455 ft spans. To meet Admiralty requirements, rail level was to be 100 ft above water level and seventeen ap-proach spans varying from 69 ft to 93 ft were required.

The two great trusses are wrought iron tubes, 16 ft across by 9 ft high; these form parabolic arches with their ends tied by suspension chains, which consist of two tiers of wrought iron links on each side of the tubes. Nearly half of the 20 ft long by 7 in. deep links were originally made for the Clifton Suspension Bridge (HEW 129).[2,3] Thus the pull of the suspension chains resists the thrust of the arches over-head. The rise of the arch equals the drop of the chains, giving an overall truss depth of 56 ft. The tubes of the two trusses are joined over the central pier where the bearings are fixed. Expansion bearings are provided at the outer sides.

The central pier is a circular column of masonry with a 35 ft diameter and is 96 ft high from bedrock to high water level surmounted by four octagonal cast-iron columns 100 ft high to rail level. It was founded by first sinking a wrought iron cylinder to bedrock using compressed air to exclude the water. This technique had been developed by John D'Urban Hughes for the Rochester Bridge (HEW 1604, p.221). The cutting edge of the cylinder was inclined to match the rock profile which had been accurately plotted from many borings. On the suggestion of R. P. Brereton, Brunel's assistant, the compressed air was only applied to an annular space around the circumference of the cylinder. When the cylinder reached solid rock, a ring of granite ashlar masonry was built in the annular space to act as a seal. The compressed air was taken off and the internal

Royal Albert Bridge, Saltash. From *The Engineer*, 147, 1929

excavation, followed by the pier construction, was in free air. The foundation work took over three years.

The trusses were fabricated on shore, parallel to the river on the Devon side. Small docks were cut under their ends to permit the entry of pontoons which lifted the trusses on a rising tide. The first truss was warped across the river into position on the Cornish side so that it rested on the tops of the masonry piers as the tide fell. Thereafter it was jacked up in 3 ft lifts, followed by lifts of cast-iron sections on the central pier and of masonry for the shore piers.

Prince Albert officially opened the bridge on 3 May 1859. Brunel was too ill to attend but he crossed the bridge a few days later lying on a specially prepared wagon. He died on 15 September 1859. Shortly afterwards the directors had the inscription 'I. K. Brunel, Engineer', placed over the shore archway in large raised letters.

The approach spans were renewed during 1928–29 and further renewals and additions of bracings to the main spans have been made for increased train loads.

1. PUGSLEY SIR A. (ed.). *The works of Isambard Kingdom Brunel: an engineering appreciation.* Institution of Civil Engineers and University of Bristol, London and Bristol, 1976, 163–182.

2. Ibid., 51–68.

3. SIVEWRIGHT W. J. (ed.). *Civil engineering heritage: Wales and western England.* Thomas Telford, London, 1986, 90–91.

13. Torpoint Chain Ferry

♣

HEW 1485

SX 442 551 to

Following his successful completion of a floating bridge or chain ferry over 550 yd at Dartmouth (HEW 1498, p.63), James Rendel was asked, in 1831, by ferry proprieters, to build a similar crossing over the 850 yd wide Hamoaze from Torpoint to Devonport.[1] The idea had developed from a proposal by James Nasmyth for pulling a boat along a fixed chain which Rendel used both for propulsion and guidance. He designed a flat-bottomed wooden vessel, 55 ft long and 45 ft wide with three hulls fixed together side by side, the outer two carrying the traffic and the inner containing the steam power plant. Guidance and haulage was obtained by two chains across the river running over 7 ft 6 in. diameter wheels with sockets around the rims shaped to accept the chain links. These wheels were keyed to a common shaft and driven by two condensing steam engines.

Above: Torpoint modern ferry

The chains and anchorages were designed for a 5 knot current, the normal spring tide flow being a little under 4 knots. To enable the chains to lie on the river bed and yet have a minimum of end slack they were kept in tension by 5 ton weights lying in 20 ft deep shafts at the top of the roadway ramps. These ramps were set at a gradient of 1 in 12 and were about 250 ft long, to accommodate the 18 ft spring tidal range. The ferry had hinged ramps at each end, lowered to and raised from the landing ramp by the engines.

The chain ferry was commissioned in 1834 and two years later a second unit enabled them to work alternate months. The crossing time was 8 minutes. Chain ferries remain in operation at Torpoint and also at Trelissick, the King Harry ferry near Truro Dartmouth, Sandbanks near Poole and at Cowes. The modern crossing at Torpoint has three ferries and chains are still used to guide them across the Hamoaze. The chains are passed on the outside of the boat, the vehicles are carried in four lanes between the outer superstructures which give shelter to passengers and a driving cabin for the crew. Other modern developments have been diesel and electric power, and elsewhere, steel wire ropes for guidance and propulsion by screw or paddle wheel independent of the guidance system.

1. RENDEL J. M. Torpoint–Devonport floating bridge. *Trans Instn Civ. Engrs*, 1838, **2**, 213–227.

14. Devonport Dockyard South Yard: No. 1 Dock and Basin, the Swing Bridge, the Scrieve Board and Slip No. 1

♦

No. 1 Dock and Basin:
HEW 1117
SX 448 544

The Swing Bridge:
HEW 285
SX 447 542

The Scrieve Board:
HEW 1119
SX 448 541

Slip No. 1 The Covered Slip:
HEW 1118
SX 452 540

No. 1 Dock is located on the western side of Devonport's South Yard.[1] Present facilities were constructed in the 1830s on the site of the yard's first dry dock, which was built between 1691 and 1693. Designed by Edmund Dummer, Naval Officer and Surveyor of the Navy, it comprised an outer basin, 256 ft by 200 ft and an inner graving dock, 170 ft by 40 ft 6 in. wide and 19 ft deep. Lock gates led from the Hamoaze to the basin and thence to the dock, the steps and altars of which were shaped to ship contours. The scheme, based on similar works at Toulon, was important in the development of dock facilities.

A little to the south is the Camber, which is crossed half way down its length by a gently arched cast-iron swing bridge of about 40 ft span. It has the words 'Horseley Ironworks (1838) near Birmingam' cast on its outer rib. The two sections were manually pivotted on a series of small wheels set on top of two substantial masonry bases projecting into the camber. It is 8½ ft wide with a plank walkway supported on four cross-braced iron ribs. The bridge is now fixed and only used by pedestrians.

Again to the south, are two covered slipways. The first is known as the Scrieve Board and probably dates from the 1830s. It is 291 ft long and 103 ft wide and its original wooden construction is now clad with corrugated metal. The original slip has been floored over. The second, No. 1 or The Covered Slip, is located adjacent to the dockyard wall. It is the oldest covered slipway of any Royal Dockyard with the slip dating from around 1763 and its covering dates from around 1814. It is 174 ft long and its roof is supported on a double line of 23 trussed wooden pillars. At the north end the roof is apsidal to accommodate bowsprits. It has undergone relatively few alterations, although the slipway was relaid in 1941 and is still used as originally intended.

Royal William
Victualling Yard

1. PRESSWELL P. T. *Ancient monuments and historic buildings, H.M. Naval Base, Devonport*. Department of the Environment PSA/MoD Joint Planning Team Publication, HMSO, 1975, 76,77,82–90.

15. Royal William Victualling Yard, Plymouth

HEW 1486

SX 462 534

Historically, this is an important group of industrial buildings.[1] In 1822 John Rennie was completing the breakwater in Plymouth Sound (HEW 126) when land at Devil's Point was chosen for a centralised Naval victualling establishment and the Navy Board engaged him to be responsible for design and construction.[2]

In the 1825 Parliamentary Navy estimates, £291 512 was allocated for the construction of a tidal basin, wharves, brewery, flour mill, bakery, cooperage, slaughterhouse, quadrangle storehouses, five houses for senior officers, porter's lodge, offices, boundary walls, drains, cranes and a reservoir.

Thousands of tons of limestone were blasted to form a level area of 14 acres on the peninsula's sheltered north side. Construction, carried out by contractor Hugh McIntosh, was in Devonian limestone with granite detailing and lasted from November 1827 to the end of 1832. Inside the buildings there was extensive use of cast-iron columns and wrought iron principal joists for upper floors and roof members. Roofs were slate with copper bonnets. A close viewpoint is obtained from the Stonehouse to Cremyll ferry.

1. Coad J. G. *The Royal dockyards 1690–1850*. Scholar Press, Aldershot, 1989, 282–292.

2. Rennie sir J. *The autobiography of Sir John Rennie*. Spon, London, 1875, 410.

16. Chelson Meadow

HEW 1040

SX 510 550

Saltram House, to the east of Plymouth, now belongs to the National Trust. In 1806, after consulting John Rennie, Lord Boringdon of Saltram contracted with James Green of Birmingham for the construction of an embankment to reclaim nearly 180 acres of land within the Plym estuary. Green had worked for his father and, since 1800, for Rennie.

The work at Saltram was carried out between 1806 and 1807. The embankment is 970 yd long, of average height 16 ft above the mud of the River Plym. The average base and crest widths are respectively 91 ft and 3 ft. It was originally intended to make the outer slope 1 in 4 and the inner slope 2 in 3 but Green made careful enquiries regarding flood levels which led him to raise the embankment's crest level and increase the slopes.

The work cost £9000 and a further £5000 was spent on maintenance between 1808 and 1842. Lord Boringdon was awarded a gold medal by the Royal Society of Arts for his achievement. The reclaimed land, which was greatly impregnated with salt, has since been used as a racecourse and, before and during World War I, as an airfield. It has recently been raised by controlled tipping.

17. Plymouth Breakwater

♦

HEW 126

SX 464 505 to 480 504

During the eighteenth century, the Royal Navy became increasingly concerned with the threat to Plymouth Sound anchorage from gales. Consequently John Rennie, senior, in collaboration with Joseph Whidbey, a naval officer, was engaged to design Plymouth Breakwater.[1]

It is an offshore embankment of limestone blocks weighing up to 7 tons tipped on rocky shoals across the entrance to the sound. The crest and part of the slope above low water are paved with limestone. The crest, set 2 ft above high water of spring tides, is unusual in that it has no protective wall above. Additional wave protection

Plymouth Breakwater location plan

is afforded by 100 ton mass concrete blocks placed on the forward slope. Of 5100 ft overall length, the breakwater comprises a central 3000 ft portion and two equal arms turning inshore at an angle of 15° to the main line. The western extremity carries a lighthouse and the eastern end a beacon, both built of granite. The deep water channel passes the western end.

Sir John Rennie supervised the work after his father's death in 1821 and modified the design by inserting a course of dovetailed granite blocks at low water level to inhibit the rubble being dragged down by wave action. He also flattened the seaward slope to 1 in 5 above low water.

Begun in 1812 and providing effective protection by 1814,[2] the breakwater required substantial additional material to make up for displacement and consolidation. By 1847, around 3 600 000 tons of stone had been dumped.

1. VERNON-HARCOURT L. F. *Harbours and docks*. Clarendon, Oxford, 1885, 186-188.

2. TOWNSHEND B. *Plymouth Breakwater*. Plymouth, 1899, 6.

18. Eddystone Lighthouse, Smeaton Tower: Substructure and Superstructure

♣

HEW 73

Substructure:
SX 383 336

Superstructure:
SX 478 538

Smeaton's Lighthouse was the third on the Eddystone rocks.[1,2] The first, by Henry Winstanley in 1698, was destroyed by storm in 1703 and the second, by John Rudyerd completed in 1708, was burnt down in 1755. Both were constructed of timber.

Trinity House then invited John Smeaton FRS to design and supervise the construction of a new tower.(See cover illustration.) He modelled its shape on the oak tree, a wide base diminishing upwards in a curved taper to offer minimum resistance to sea and wind with a low centre of gravity. It was 72 ft high and about 25 ft diameter at the base. He chose Portland stone faced with Cornish granite. The stones, weighing up to 2½ tons, were cut to template and trial fitted at a yard at Millbay, Plymouth. The blocks were interlocking and secured to courses above and below by oak trenails and marble joggles.

Courses were bedded on a mortar of lime and pozzolana which set under water and which Smeaton had developed experimentally.

The first stones were laid on 12 June 1757 at a level of 9 ft below high water of spring tides and the structure was completed on 16 October 1759. The lighthouse operated until 1882 when it was replaced because of deterioration of the rock base, first observed in 1878. After the present tower (HEW 74) was brought into use, Smeaton's was taken down to plinth level and re-erected on Plymouth Hoe, where it may now be visited by the public. It is commemorated in the crest of the Institution of Civil Engineers.

1. SKEMPTON A. W. (ed.). *John Smeaton FRS.* Thomas Telford, London, 1981, 83–102.

2. SMEATON J. *A narrative of the building and a description of the construction of the Eddystone Lighthouse.* London, 1791, 2nd edn. 1793, 3rd edn 1813.

19. Eddystone Lighthouse, Douglass Tower

◆

In 1877, on the advice of James Douglass, Engineer-in-Chief, Trinity House decided to erect a new lighthouse[1] at Eddystone. Erosion of the gneiss foundation of Smeaton's tower (HEW 72) was becoming serious and, moreover, during storms the light was obliterated by waves. The new site was 120 ft south-east of Smeaton's lighthouse, which was subsequently demolished.

HEW 74

SX 383 336

The new Eddystone Lighthouse

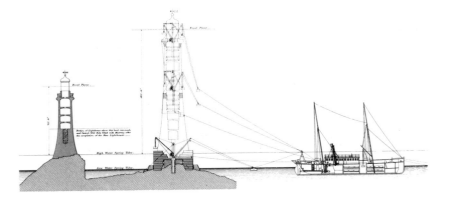

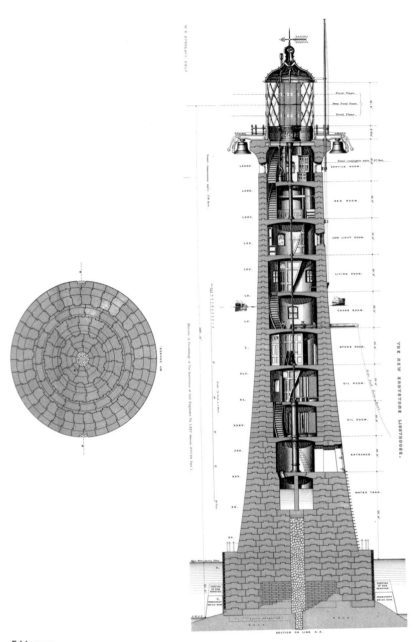

Eddystone
Lighthouse,
Douglass Tower

The lighthouse has a 44 ft diameter cylindrical base set 19 ft above low water level, the base top being used as a landing platform. The tower is a concave elliptical frustum 168 ft high and of 35 ft base diameter with the light 135 ft above mean high water level. Except for the water tank, the first 25 ft of the tower is solid and then the wall thickness diminishes upwards from 8 ft 6 in. to 2 ft 3 in. below the lantern. The light has a range of 17 miles.

As the lowest tender was in excess of the estimate, direct labour was used. Thomas Edmond was Superintendent for Erection and William Tregarthen Douglass was the Assistant Engineer. As the base was founded below low water, a brick cofferdam was built. This could be dewatered in 15 minutes by the pumps in the tender *Hercules* which brought all the prepared masonry and stores from a workyard at Oreston, Plymouth. There are 2171 pieces of masonry containing 62 133 ft^3 of granite, each block for the tower being dovetailed top, bottom and on the sides. The lowest course was secured to the rock base by Muntz metal bolts.

The Duke of Edinburgh, Master of Trinity House, opened the lighthouse on 18 May 1882. The following month Douglass received a Knighthood on the completion of this, his best known work.

1. Douglass W. T. The new Eddystone Lighthouse. *Min. Proc. Instn Civ. Engrs*, 1884, **75**, 20–60.

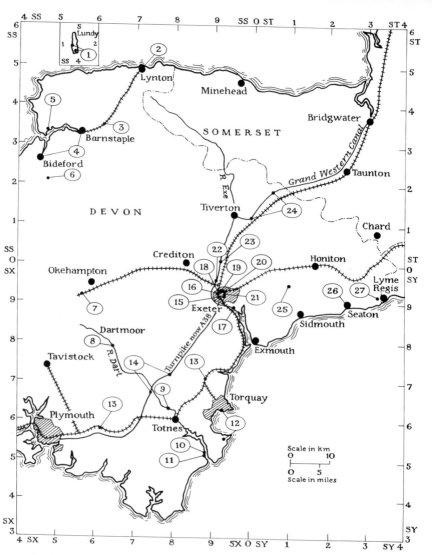

1. The Lundy Lighthouses
2. Lynton Cliff Railway
3. Chelfham Viaduct, Lynton and
   Barnstaple Railway
4. Barnstaple and Bideford Bridges
5. Braunton Marsh
6. Beam Aqueduct, Torrington
7. Meldon Viaduct
8. Postbridge, Clapper Bridge
9. Staverton Bridge
10. Higher Ferry, Dartmouth

11. The Newcomen Memorial Engine
12. Brixham Breakwater, Torquay
    Harbour
13. The South Devon Railway
14. Exeter to Plymouth Turnpike Road
15. Medieval Exe Bridge
16. Moving a fifteenth century building
17. Exeter Canal
18. Cathedral Close Footbridge
19. Iron bridge, North Street

20. The Underground Passages
21. Reinforced Concrete Church
22. Cowley Bridge
23. Thorverton Bridge
24. Grand Western Canal, Halber
    Aqueduct
25. St Saviour's Bridge, Ottery St
26. Axmouth Bridge
27. Cannington Viaduct

52

3. Central and Eastern Devon

Central and eastern Devon is largely agricultural in character and has no dominant industry, but the natural attractions of both coastlines and of the interior have enabled tourism to develop and thrive. The area's northern coastline is generally steep and rugged with very few harbours. However, the estuaries of the Taw and Torridge enabled ports to be established at Barnstaple and Bideford from early times. Both towns have impressive multi-span masonry arch bridges crossing their rivers. The southern coastline is significantly more varied in character and is punctuated by a number of estuaries. There are numerous ports, like Torquay and Brixham with its Rendel breakwater, which now largely serve the needs of local fishing and leisure interests. Several examples of land reclamation are sited within the estuaries, typified by the early nineteenth century recovery of Braunton Marsh.

Exeter's original water supply came from springs to the north-east from whence it was conveyed by a series of tunnels to the Cathedral and medieval city. The port of Exeter was established by building the nation's earliest pound lock canal in 1566 which joined the navigable River Exe just upstream of the Countess Wear Bridge. The Grand Western Canal, built by John Rennie in 1814, traverses the area from Tiverton to the Devon–Somerset border.

The area contains important examples of aspects of bridge development. Eight spans of the thirteenth century masonry crossing of the Exe are preserved in Exeter. Staverton Bridge, with seven spans of around 20 ft, was constructed two centuries later. Postbridge's date of construction is unknown but its use of large unhewn stone slabs, or clappers, represents a rudimentary construction form. Cowley Bridge, of 1814, with its three masonry spans of around 50 ft, illustrates the increase in span length from those traditionally employed. Exeter's footbridge, also of 1814, and the city's six- span viaduct of 1835 are both examples of the use of cast iron in bridge building. The subsequent use of concrete is shown in the Cannington Viaduct of 1903 and the Axmouth Bridge at Seaton, built in 1877, which is one of the oldest surviving concrete structures of its type. A relatively early example of this composite material's use in building work is shown at Exeter's Sidwell Street Church.

An early railway, using granite slabs to support the track, can be found at Haytor on Dartmoor and although many other railways, like the Lynton and Barnstaple, with its impressive Chelfham Viaduct, significantly contributed to the area's transport system, the most important nineteenth century development was the arrival of Brunel's Bristol and Exeter railway in 1844 and its subsequent 52 mile extension to Plymouth connecting via the Royal Albert Bridge with Cornwall's railways. There are a number of important engineering features on the Devon section including the 62-span masonry arch viaduct incorporating St Thomas station at Exeter and 3 miles of masonry sea wall enabling the line to be constructed adjacent to the sea approaching Teignmouth. The railway was designed to use Brunel's innovative and controversial atmospheric traction system which, it was thought, would enable a steeper gradient to be used. The pumping station at Starcross remains as one reminder of the unsuccessful experiment, abandoned in 1848, which also left the route with four of the steepest inclines on Britain's main line railways.

Lynton Cliff Railway

1. The Lundy Lighthouses

♦

Built in 1820, the first two lighthouses on Lundy were sited on the island's high ground at elevations of 538 and 508 ft above sea-level. They were frequently obscured by fog and were replaced in 1893 when Thomas Matthews, Engineer-in-Chief of Trinity House, established the north and south lighthouses in use today.

HEW 1429

SS 130 481 and

The lighthouse at the north-west point of the island has a circular white tower and is 56 ft high to the gallery, which is 165 ft above sea-level. The light, modernised in 1970–71 by I. C. Clingan, the Engineer-in-Chief, is a fourth order dioptric of 600 000 candle power.

At the south-east point of the island the lighthouse also has a circular white tower 52 ft high to the gallery which is 175 ft above sea-level. The light is a fourth order dioptric of 576 000 candlepower. In 1989 a ground helicopter pad was added. Lundy Island is now owned by the National Trust.

2. Lynton Cliff Railway

♣

The Lynton Cliff railway, said to be Britain's 'longest and most interesting'[1] is 862 ft long and runs from Lynton to Lynmouth over a vertical height of 430 ft. The 3 ft 9 in. gauge track is secured to the rock face by steel sleepers made out of inverted rails set in concrete. Two cars are permanently linked by a wire rope and travel on double track railway arranged to give passing clearance at mid-length. A triangular tank under each carriage carries 700 gallons of water ballast which is supplied from the West Lyn river intake 1 mile away. Operation is by release of water from the lower car's tank. The hydraulic buffer at the bottom end of the track is claimed to be the original design.

HEW 1109

SS 720 496

Financed by Sir George Newnes, designed and built by Robert Jones of Lynton and opened on 9 April 1890, the railway was originally used to carry goods brought in by sea such as coal, ice, sand, granite, barrelled petrol and paraffin. The carriages were converted from platforms to passenger vehicles in 1947.

1. Day J. R. and Wilson B. G. *Unusual railways*. Frederick Muller, London, 1957, 73.

3. Chelfham Viaduct, Lynton and Barnstaple Railway

♠

HEW 1028

SS 609 356

The Lynton and Barnstaple Railway,[1,2] the West Country's only narrow (1 ft 11½ in.) gauge passenger carrying line was opened on 16 May 1898 to link Lynton and Lynmouth with other railways. It had great tourist potential but some disadvantages. Lynton's station was sited 250 ft above the town and was therefore relatively inaccessible. Also the line's 19 mile length proved too far for the uncomfortable conditions of a narrow gauge line. The journey time to Lynton was nearly 2 hours, due largely to 8 miles at a 1 in 50 gradient.

Although the line became part of the Southern Railway in 1922 it could not compete with road alternatives

Chelfam Viaduct

and was closed and dismantled in 1935. In 1952, the Lynmouth floods tore out an underbridge and part of an embankment at Parracombe. Chelfham Viaduct remains as an outstanding structure, both of the Lynton and Barnstaple Railway and of any narrow gauge line nationwide. It has eight yellow brick arches of 24 ft span supported by tapering brick piers with masonry lower sections. The viaduct is straight over most of its length but has a curve at the southern end. The parapets have been removed to about 1 ft above ballast level. The structure is about 133 yd long, 70 ft high and is Listed Grade II.

1. BROWN G. A. et al. *The Lynton and Barnstaple Railway*. David and Charles, Newton Abbot, 1964.

2. CATCHPOLE L. T. *Lynton and Barnstaple Railway*. Oakwood Press, Sidcup, 1963.

4. Barnstaple Bridge and Bideford Bridge

Both Barnstaple[1] and Bideford[2] road bridges are medieval and were owned by bridge trusts until the 1960s; they are Ancient Monuments and Listed Grade I.

Barnstaple Bridge :
HEW 1450
SS 558 329

Bideford is the longer with 24 pointed arches varying in span from 12 ft to 25 ft. It was originally constructed in timber around 1286 but masonry was placed over and around the timber in about 1500. The thickness of the piers varies from 9 ft to 12 ft. Widening was carried out from 1792 onwards by placing segmental arches springing from the cutwaters against the spandrels of the original arches; this work was completed by James Green by 1810. In 1864, footways were built using iron girders supported from the cutwaters which enabled the full 16 ft width of the masonry structure to be used for traffic. In 1925, under the direction of Sir Douglas Fox and Partners, the cutwaters were rebuilt, the ironwork removed and 7 ft wide reinforced concrete footways built on each side of the roadway.

Bideford Bridge :
HEW 862
SS 456 263

In 1968, the two arches nearest the Town Wall collapsed under flood water. The Department of Transport took ownership and Messrs Freeman Fox and Partners designed replacement arches and carried out extensive repairs to the whole structure. These included the provi-

Barnstaple Bridge

sion of small diameter concrete piles through all the piers to give a continuous grout curtain to 12 ft below the river bed level. In 1987 a new high level bridge over the river Torridge to the north relieved Bideford Bridge of trunk road traffic.

Barnstaple Bridge has 16 pointed masonry arches with spans ranging from 18 ft to 26 ft and appears to have been constructed in masonry around 1280 for, in 1333, there is a document referring to masonry repairs. Partly destroyed in 1437 and 1646, the bridge was first widened in 1796 by the construction of segmental arches springing from the cutwaters. It was further widened in 1832–34, by James Green, who installed 4 ft wide footways on cantilevered ironwork supplied by the Neath Abbey Iron Company at a cost of £4000. At this time the roadway became 16 ft wide.

In 1949 R. M. Stone, the Trust's Engineer, protected the piers by steel sheet piling with the spaces filled by cement grout under pressure by the Cementation Company. In 1961 the Department of Transport assumed bridge ownership and in 1963, Messrs Posford, Pavry and Partners widened the bridge on the upstream side only, giving two 6 ft footways and a 24 ft wide carriageway; Messrs Cementation again carried out the work. The 1834 ironwork was removed and masonry parapets built so that the downstream elevation is now as it was between 1796 and 1832. In 1978 the downstream view of the bridge was improved by the removal of the adjacent steel railway bridge as a consequence of the closure of the Barnstaple to Ilfracombe branch line. In 1989 a new bridge over the river Taw on the town's southern edge has relieved Barnstaple bridge of trunk road traffic.

1. CRUSE J. B. *The long bridge of Barnstaple and the Bridge Trust.* Aycliffe Press, Barnstaple, 1982.

2. WHITING F. E. *The long bridge of Bideford.* The Bridge Feof Fees, 1945.

5. Braunton Marsh

♣

HEW 1452

SS 469 329 to 486 357

At the time of Devon's first Ordnance Survey in 1809, Braunton Marsh was shown as tidal but the Burrows and the Great Field were not. In 1806–7 James Green had demonstrated to Lord Boringdon his skill with earth embankments in the Plym and Kingsbridge estuaries. At Braunton he proposed a scheme for Lord Rolle and other landowners, whereby he would construct a 4000 yd embankment from the Burrows to Velator Bridge alongside the Braunton Pill.

A survey of the marsh by Green and John Pascoe in 1808 led to the Braunton Land Enclosure Act of 23 May 1811 and works were completed by around 1814. As at Chelson Meadow (HEW 1040, p.46), the embankments sloped at approximately 1 in 4 on the estuarial side and 1 in 1½ on the landward side with a 6 ft wide crest. A

Braunton Marsh outlet

tidal outlet was built at SS 477 342 which now discharges into Horsey Island. In 1857 N. Whitley, a Truro surveyor, reclaimed the further 400 acres known as Horsey Island which completed the reclamation work between the Burrows and the Pill. Approximately 1300 acres were enclosed by Green's work and this extensive grazing area is now administered by the Braunton Land Drainage Commissioners. Together, these works are probably the most significant estuarial reclamation in Devon.

♣

HEW 384

SS 473 209

Beam Aqueduct, Torrington

6. Beam Aqueduct, Torrington

In 1823 James Green prepared a scheme for a canal leading from the River Torridge, opposite Weare Giffard, to the town mills upstream of Torrington. It was built for Lord Rolle, at his own expense and without Parliamentary approval. The canal was at an elevated level reached by an inclined plane and this enabled it to cross the river on a substantial five-span masonry arched aqueduct, 2 miles downstream of Torrington and close to Beam House.

Thereafter the canal ran level until it reached the take-off from the river just above the town mills.[1]

The five arches are each 31 ft span and the aqueduct is 23 ft between the parapets. The first stone was laid on 11 August 1824. This is a graceful structure, 55 ft high, having rectangular piers with rounded ends to arch springing level and tapered semicircular columns above. The semicircular arch rings and string course are plain, as is the parapet, except for square refuges above the semicircular columns.

In 1871 a branch of the London and South Western Railway was built over parts of the canal bed and the railway from Bideford to Torrington was opened in July 1872. The aqueduct has now been converted to a road bridge and forms part of the driveway to Beam College.

1. HADFIELD C. *Canals of south west England*. David and Charles, Newton Abbot, 1967, 135–141.

7. Meldon Viaduct

HEW 270

SS 564 923

The London and South Western Railway route around the north and west of Dartmoor from Exeter to Plymouth contained many viaducts. The most impressive lies 2 miles south-west of Okehampton over the valley of the River Okement.[1] It stands 144 ft above river bed level.

There are two separate and parallel structures designed by W. R. Galbraith, each with six spans to horizontal curves of about 1980 ft radius. One was built in 1874, the other in 1879. The spans of both structures comprise two 90 ft Warren girders. The trusses are at 5 ft, 7 ft 6 in. and 5 ft centres and are 9 ft 4 in. high with the older trusses having a bottom tension member of a vertical flat only.

The piers, ranging in height from 48 ft to 120 ft, are formed of four wrought iron columns, in sections 10 ft 6 in. long, braced horizontally and diagonally at each joint. The column sections are made in six parts with longitudinal rivetted joints and rest on 24 ft wide masonry bases. The piers of the first viaduct were strengthened in 1959 when collars were placed around the columns and heavier bracing installed.

Through railway traffic ceased on 6 May 1968. Since then the viaduct has been used for conveying aggregates by road vehicle to the construction site of the Meldon Dam, a 167 ft high gravity concrete structure completed in 1972. Both viaducts and dam can be viewed from a car park and picnic area at map reference SX 562 919, approached from Okehampton through Meldon village.

1. THOMAS D. St J. *West Country railway history*. David and Charles, Newton Abbott, 1973, 103–4.

♣ 8. Postbridge Clapper Bridge

HEW 637

SX 648 788

This bridge, near Moretonhampstead, is a fine example of a medieval clapper bridge, of which there are several in Devon and Somerset (e.g. Tarr Steps HEW 863, p.92). None are dated before the thirteenth century. It crosses the East Dart river just south of the B3212 road and has raised abutments and piers with three spans, of 12 ft 9 in., 9 ft and 11 ft from east to west. The piers, of large unmortared stones, are 11 ft long and 3 ft 3 in. wide. The east pier is 6 courses high, with three stones per course in the pier length. The west pier is 7 courses high, of which two have only two stones in the length. The bridge is decked by rough hewn slabs, the 'clappers', about 1 ft thick, to give a width of between 7 and 8 ft. From soffit to bed level is about 9 ft at the piers. There are deep steps down to ground level at each end to join the riverside footpaths. The joints between the ends of the deck slabs have been mortared and there is some mortaring at the approach steps. Otherwise the bridge remains of dry stone construction. It is a Scheduled Ancient Monument.

♣ 9. Staverton Bridge

HEW 1601

SX 784 637

In 1413 an Indulgence was granted by Bishop Stafford of Exeter for the construction of Staverton Bridge.[1] It lay on the road from Ashburton, one of the four Devon stannery towns, to Totnes, at the head of the tidal portion of the River Dart. The route was not superseded until the middle of the nineteenth century, when Riverford Bridge was built and now carries the A384 from Buckfastleigh to Totnes.

Nearly 220 ft in overall length, Staverton Bridge has seven semicircular, slightly pointed, single ring arches,

Staverton Bridge

five are about 21 ft span and two about 16 ft span. Each springs from about 2 ft above low water level. Rises are 11 ft for the larger arches and 8 ft for the smaller. The depth at low water varies from 2 ft under the smaller arches to 6 ft under the larger. Each pier is approximately 11 ft wide with a pointed cutwater extending up to the solid parapet as a pedestrian refuge. The road width is 10 ft. The bridge is Listed Grade I and is a Scheduled Ancient Monument.

1. HENDERSON C. and JERVOISE E. *Old Devon bridges*. Wheaton, Exeter, 1938, 35–6.

10. Higher Ferry, Dartmouth

The A379, Exeter to Plymouth road, crosses the River Dart at Dartmouth, where there had been an ancient passenger ferry. In the nineteenth century, James M. Rendel was asked to prepare an improvement scheme and initially proposed a suspension bridge to cross the river width. This was blocked by a local landowner, James Elton, and Rendel then proposed a chain ferry

HEW 1498

SX 879 519 to 881 552

Higher Ferry, Dartmouth

using an idea of James Nasmyth for pulling a vessel along a fixed chain.[1]

The ferry, Rendel's first, comprised two pontoons side-by-side and a steam engine between them, that hauled on a chain using a wheel with sockets that were recessed around the rim and shaped to receive the chain links. The chain was adjusted for length at each end by a weight in a vertical shaft, so that it would normally be on the river bed and yet be sufficiently taut to maintain the ferry's direction. The pulley weight also tended to reduce shock loadings. Two chains were used when the ferry commenced operation, so the wheels, located outside the pontoons, were connected to the steam engine by a shaft passing transversely under the deck.

On land, the highway was ramped at both ends to enable the ferry to be independent of the tide. The ferry had hinged ramps at each end which were lowered onto the fixed ramps for embarkation and disembarkation of vehicles. Construction commenced in March 1831 and the ferry was opened in August of the same year. Isaac Blackburn of Turnchapel built the hulls and John Mare of Plymouth supplied the machinery. The present ferry, built in 1960, has a capacity of 18 motor cars, is guided by two steel ropes, one on either side, and is propelled by paddle wheels driven by a diesel engine.

Rendel was subsequently responsible for the design of several other chain ferries including those at Saltash, Torpoint (HEW 1485, p.43), Woolston (Southampton) and Portsmouth.[2]

1. PERKINS K. S. The puffing giant. *Devon Historian*, April 1985, 4–8.

2. RENDEL J. M. Obit. *Min. Proc. Instn Civ. Engrs*, 1856–57, **16**, 133–142.

11. Newcomen Memorial Engine ♣

HEW 1174

SX 878 515

Thomas Newcomen, a Dartmouth ironmonger, set out to improve the pumps used in Devon tin mines. He developed what he termed a non-rotative fire engine, coupled by a beam to a reciprocating pump at the bottom of a mine shaft. The power stroke came from the vacuum caused by condensing steam within a piston. After ten years of development work, during which time the tin mines failed, his first engine was installed at a coal mine near Dudley in 1712. It was successful and over a 20 year period 100 were built, a figure which ultimately grew to some 2000.

The Newcomen Memorial Engine at Dartmouth also worked in a Midlands colliery but was transferred to Hawkesbury Canal Junction near Coventry in 1821 to pump canal feeder water. It worked at a rate of 12 strokes per minute and delivered 15 000 gallons of water per hour. After working until 1913, it was handed over in 1963 by the British Transport Commission to the Newcomen Society for preservation and was erected by Mr Arthur Pyne at Dartmouth as a memorial marking the 300th anniversary of Newcomen's birth.

The engine has a 22 in. diameter vertical cylinder set above a condenser supplied by a cold water injection tank and discharges to a condensate outlet below. To avoid distortion the piston rod is connected by a chain to a quadrant at one end of a 12 ft rocker beam supported on an 'A' frame. A similar quadrant and chain at the other end of the beam connect to the pump plunger rod and piston. Because the pump cylinder is at ground level, instead of at the bottom of a mine shaft, a weight is added to the pump plunger to ensure that it will fall by gravity on the return stroke. The steam and water valves operate automatically.

♣

Brixham
Breakwater:
HEW 1487
SX 931 566

Torquay
Harbour:
HEW 1640
SX 917 633

12. Brixham Breakwater and Torquay Harbour

Torbay naturally provides shelter from westerly gales which has led towns, such as Brixham and Torquay, to construct harbour facilities. Sheltered by Berry Head, Brixham Harbour developed after 1836 when James Rendel produced a report and drawings for a breakwater. An Act was obtained and a length of 1400 ft was built in 1843, until money ran out. In 1909 some 600 ft were built

Torquay Harbour

at a cost of £23 000 and in 1912 another 1000 ft were started; they were completed in 1916 at a cost of £40 000. With this shelter, Brixham developed as a fishing port with convenient rail access to London. The breakwater was built using block limestone quarried from the adjacent Berry Head and deposited in the bay. The seaward side only was faced with jointed masonry.

At Torquay, an inner harbour was built in 1806 and the Haldon Pier in 1870. The latter was constructed from concrete blocks 10 or 13 ft long by 4 ft wide and 4 ft high placed on the sea bed by divers. The pier extended to the south-west from Beacon Hill, which was excavated to provide the broken stone aggregate and to form a level standing. P. J. Margary was the Resident Engineer. In 1886 Torquay Corporation acquired the anchorage and its environs from Lord Haldon, whose family had built the piers. Further improvements, such as the Princess Pier to enclose the outer harbour and the filling in of the landward side, have been carried out subsequently. In the nineteenth century the harbour provided access to naval vessels sheltering in the bay but subsequently it has mainly acted as a base for pleasure trips along the coast and to the Channel Islands.

Opposite:
Brixham Harbour

♠

13. The South Devon Railway

HEW 1353

SX 911 933 to

In 1843 the Great Western, the Bristol and Exeter and the Bristol and Gloucester Railways combined to support a project to build 52 miles of railway from Exeter to Plymouth. The Bill for the South Devon Railway[1-3] (SDR) received Royal Assent on 7 July 1844 and I. K. Brunel was appointed Engineer.

Brunel chose a route avoiding the Haldon Hills, south-west of Exeter, by following the Exe estuary, thence the coast from Dawlish Warren to Teignmouth and the Teign estuary to Newton Abbot. From here the route went on to Aller, whence a branch was to run to Torre, on the outskirts of Torquay. He had previously surveyed a route crossing the Teign and Dart but was deterred by the cost of bridging the estuaries. Instead he chose a route across the southern edge of Dartmoor which involved a climb of 250 ft from Aller to Dainton, at a maximum gradient of 1 in 38, before falling almost as steeply to cross the Dart at Totnes. A slightly easier climb, but nearly 5 miles long, brought the line up Rattery bank and by gentler gradients to a summit at Wrangaton, 446 ft above sea-level. From here, the line fell by easy gradients to Hemerdon, whence the line dropped by a 2 miles long, 1 in 42 bank to the Plym estuary at Plympton.

Brunel had been impressed by a demonstration of an atmospheric system of traction, in which the train was drawn by a piston in a tube between the rails from which air was evacuated by a series of pumping stations along the route. It appeared that as there was no heavy locomotive, the arrangement was specially suitable for steep gradients. It was already in use on two short lines, the London and Croydon and the Kingstown (Dun Laoghaire) to Dalkey in Ireland.

At the company's first meeting in August 1844 it was decided to use the atmospheric system. Soon after, a start was made on line construction and after winter gales had delayed the building of the river and sea-walls, the line was opened from Exeter to Teignmouth in May 1846 and on to Newton Abbot seven months later.

However, as the atmospheric system was not yet ready, steam locomotives had to be hired for several months. Atmospheric traction started to be used between

Exeter and Teignmouth in September 1847 and on to Newton Abbot in January 1848. By this time the railway had been opened to Totnes in July 1847 and the atmospheric equipment, including pumping stations at Dainton and Totnes, had been installed. But this was never used as it proved impossible to maintain the vacuum economically and at a shareholder's meeting on 31 August 1848 it was resolved to abandon the system. By then the line had been opened to Laira, on the outskirts of Plymouth. It was extended to the Millbay terminus in April 1849, opened between Aller Junction and Torre in December 1848 and a branch was completed from Marsh Mills, Plympton to Tavistock in 1859.

The line has a number of interesting features. Shortly after leaving Exeter it crosses low ground in the Exeter suburb of St Thomas by the 62-span masonry arch viaduct (HEW 1350, SX 91 91) incorporating St Thomas Station, which was the railway's original headquarters.

Seven miles further on, at Starcross, are the remains of one of the atmospheric pumping engine stations (HEW 792, SX 977 817) which comprised two red sandstone rectangular buildings with a square chimney. It was subsequently used as a church, a coal merchant's store and more recently as a museum of atmospheric memorabilia. Another remaining atmospheric pumping station building is at Totnes, which was subsequently used as a creamery. A third exists at Torre, but the other eight pumping stations have been demolished.

The line's most notable feature is the section between Dawlish Warren and Teignmouth, where it passes right along the coast, protected by 3 miles of masonry sea wall (HEW 793, SX 979 779 to 946 732). Founded on breccia and limestone, the wall's face is concave to provide a wave return and its top provides a sea-side walk about 15 ft above the beach for about 1 mile at each end. In between, the wall alternates with five short tunnels between 50 and 37 yd long. Over the years, damage to the wall has been superficial, though there has been some washout of ballast. Bi-directional working on the up line is available should the need arise to close the down line.

Between Rattery and Hemerdon banks, in the southern part of Dartmoor, the railway crosses five deep valleys by means of viaducts. Typical of these is that at Ivybridge (HEW 875, SX 635 568). As designed by Brunel, this was constructed of eleven bays of timber frames on masonry piers. Each frame, which was below rail level, consisted of horizontal top members supported by struts raking at low angles from the piers, the bottom tie of the frame consisting of iron rods.

When atmospheric construction was abandoned and the viaducts had to carry steam locomotives, strongly trussed parapets were added above the existing trusses. The flooring was strengthened during 1861–63 and the original structures were replaced by masonry viaducts when the line was being doubled in 1893. Ivybridge Viaduct had 11 spans of 60 ft, the other four had between five and 13 spans, also of 60 ft.

There were also six timber viaducts on the Plymouth to Tavistock line. These were similar to those on the Cornwall Railway (HEW 877). Of the 52 mile length of the railway, nearly 13 were double from the outset, from Totnes to Rattery and Hemerdon to Plymouth. Doubling of the other sections was carried out between 1855 and 1874, and when the Great Western Railway took over the SDR in 1876, only the sections between Dawlish and Teignmouth and Rattery and Hemerdon remained single.

Along with the Cornwall Railway, the SDR underwent gauge conversion in May 1892 and in the following year the Rattery to Hemerdon section was doubled and its five viaducts rebuilt with masonry arches. The Dawlish to Teignmouth section through the sea wall tunnels remained single until 1905 when the Brunel broad gauge allowed the engineers to install a travelling shield outside the standard gauge clearance and keep traffic moving while the tunnels were widened.

1. MacDermot E. T. and Clinker C. R. *History of the Great Western Railway.* 2. Ian Allan, London, 1964, 103–136,331–333.

2. Thomas D. St J. *West country railway history.* David and Charles, Newton Abbot, 1973, 77–95.

3. Pugsley sir A. *The works of Isambard Kingdom Brunel.* Institution of Civil Engineers and University of Bristol, London and Bristol, 1976, 123–126.

14. Exeter to Plymouth Turnpike Road

♠

By the early nineteenth century the Turnpike Road between Exeter and Plymouth was regarded as poorly aligned and the 1 in 8 gradients as excessive. James Green, the County Bridge Surveyor, made a report in 1819 to the Turnpike Trustees recommending a maximum gradient of 1 in 15. Some 14 miles of the total 42 mile length required realignment including the length from Chudleigh via Haldon racecourse to the Exeter to Newton road near Kennford and from South Brent to Buckfastleigh.

Among Green's recommendations was the widening of the River Dart Bridge, (SX 744 667) an Ancient Monument. He had previously built new bridges over the Rivers Teign and Yealm and further bridges were subsequently built over the Rivers Plym, Bovey and Lemon. At Bickington, near the River Lemon, a buttressed causeway 30 ft wide and 30 ft high was also required (SX 791 723). Green was also responsible for early examples of grade separation, including a bridge carrying a lane from Rattery towards the Moor and by a tunnel for cattle under the turnpike embankment at the nearby Whiteoxen Manor.

HEW 1041

SX 479 545 to 919 926

Above: Exeter to Plymouth Turnpike Road

♣ 15. Medieval Exe Bridge, Exeter

HEW 996

SX 919 921

Above: Medieval
Exe Bridge, Exeter

Along with a bridge at Fountains Abbey, Yorkshire, said to date from 1147, this is among the nation's earliest surviving bridge works. It was promoted by Nicholas and Walter Gervase and built between 1190 and 1210. Some 16 to 18 arches may have been constructed originally, but when a new three-arched masonry bridge was built on an upstream site in 1778, the portion of the old bridge which crossed the main stream of the River Exe was demolished. This left the arches which crossed the marshland on the inside river bend intact; they were eventually buried or incorporated in roads or buildings.

When twin bridges were constructed between 1968 and 1972, the old city brewery and adjoining buildings were demolished, exposing five complete arches of the medieval bridge.[1] Eventually, eight and a half arches were revealed. Most are Norman semicircular with three ribs about 3 ft wide with a rib space of about 3 ft. The pointed, or Gothic, arches have two rings and five chamfered ribs

1 ft 6 in. wide with a space of about 3 ft between them. The predominant building stone is a local vesicular volcanic rock, then obtainable from quarries in Thorverton and Ide. Small amounts of triassic sandstone occur in the base of a cutwater and cretaceous limestone from east Devon is used in some of the arches.

The bridge remains are in surroundings landscaped by the City Council's Parks Department. They are a Scheduled Ancient Monument.

1. BRIERLEY J. The medieval Exe bridge. *Proc. Instn Civ. Engrs*, 1979, Part 1, **66**, 127–39.

16. Exeter — moving a fifteenth century building

♠

A timber framed house, 16 Edmund Street, at the corner of Frog Street, was a Listed Building obstructing the intended route of a new inner city ring road. The City Council decided to move it about 100 yd to its present site. They engaged Messrs Pynford to do the work because of their known expertise in the specialist field of shoring and underpinning.

The house has three storeys, each upper storey overhanging the one below on two sides. It is about 20 ft square on plan and has a pitched, slated roof with a small front window near the apex. Before moving, the house was strutted, braced and lifted on to a timber platform with strutting from the platform to the overhanging top floor. In all, 10 tons of timber were used to encase and support the structure.

The house was moved over a two day period in December 1961 but only 4½ hours were actually spent in hauling. The remaining time was used to make fine adjustments to hydraulic jacks to level the house. Haulage was by winches and direction changes were controlled by providing rails within which the wheels could travel.

It was the first time a house of this age, *circa* 1430, had been moved and it now stands in a group of interesting older buildings close to the medieval bridge. (HEW 996). It is Listed Grade II.

HEW 794

SX 918 922

17. Exeter Canal, Trew's Weir, Warehouses and Brunel's Dragboat

♣

Exeter Canal:
HEW 529
SX 923 917 to
963 861

Trew's Weir:
HEW 606
SX 924 916

Warehouses:
HEW 1395
SX 921 921

Brunel's Drag Boat:
HEW 1145
SX 922 918

Above: Trew's Weir

In order to improve the river navigation on the Exe to Exeter, John Trew constructed the original canal between 1564 and 1566.[1,2] It was the first in the country to use pound locks. It ran 3110 yd from the city walls to just above the present Countess Wear Bridge (HEW 1803, SX 942 895), had a 16 ft top width, a 3 ft depth and took vessels up to 16 tons. Three pound locks were built with a pair of gates at the canal's seaward end.

In 1675 Richard Hurd extended the canal towards Topsham making a larger entrance, Trenchard's Sluice, for 60 ton vessels. Work completed in 1701 made the canal 50 ft wide and 10 ft deep and capable of taking 150 ton vessels. Double locks were built to replace the three locks.

In 1820 James Green built a pair of gates at the Exeter end, Kings Arms Sluice, to make a lock enabling ships to move from the canal to the river at varying river levels. He straightened the canal, made an outfall beneath the bed from the Alphin Brook to the River Exe, lowered the bottom cill of the double locks and reconstructed Trenchard's Sluice to form a lock with two sets of gates.

Brunel's Dragboat

Between 1825 and 1827 he extended the canal 2 miles to Turf where an entrance lock was built. He also constructed a lock to the river at Topsham and a new basin at Exeter to avoid deepening the river. Vessels of 14 ft draught and up to 400 tons could then be accommodated.

Two fine quayside warehouses were built near the City's Watergate entrance in 1835. They are each of five storeys, have their backs to a sandstone cliff and are constructed of masonry with slated roofs. The four upper floors and the columns are in timber. One warehouse is in dark red volcanic Pocombe stone, shot with white veins of quartz with red brick trimmings for the openings, whereas the other is in pale green limestone, using masonry at the openings.

Trew's Weir, dating from 1566, across the River Exe provided the canal's water supply. Before modernisation, the crest width was 263 ft 6 in. and the weir was about 5 ft 6 in. high from toe to crest. The weir was believed to have contributed to the flooding of Exeter in 1960 and a rising gate sluice was constructed to spill flood water downstream of the weir. A long side-weir was also built to convey flood water to a newly constructed dry channel alongside the river, which it rejoined down-stream.

Since 1960, regular use of the canal has dwindled from 55 000 tons per annum to that of a motor vessel carrying sewage sludge for sea disposal. The canal basin, its ware-houses and the former electricity works now form the Exeter Maritime Museum, which also displays *Bertha*, the Brunel Drag Boat built by the Great Western Railway for use in the River Parrett at Bridgwater in 1844. This 50 ft long iron hulled craft has an iron spade at one end which was lowered into the mud in front of the quay wall. The boat was hauled away from the wall by a chain on a large steam driven drum and the spade dragged the mud into the stream of the river to be carried away.

1. HADFIELD C. *The canals of south west England.* David and Charles, Newton Abbot, 1967, 19–25, 190–1.

2. DE LA GARDE P. C. and GREEN J. Memoir of the canal of Exeter from 1563 to 1724, continuation of the memoir 1819–30. *Min. Proc. Instn Civ. Engrs*, 1845, **4**, 90–113.

Below: Exeter
Cathedral Close
Footbridge

18. Exeter Cathedral Close Footbridge

♣

To the east of Exeter Cathedral, carrying a footpath which runs along the top of the old city wall and at the entrance to the Cathedral Close, there is an attractive decorated cast-iron footbridge built in 1814 which retains its original iron lamp brackets. Originally the footpath would have joined the Deanery gardens to the Bishop's Palace.

There are two segmental cast-iron arch ribs 4 ft 7 in. apart, of 19 ft span and 4 ft 5 in. rise. The spandrel infilling is of integrally cast diminishing circles. The wrought iron parapets are attractively designed in four panels. The original deck has been replaced by stiffened welded steel plate on rolled steel joists. The bridge is Listed as Grade II*.

HEW 362

SX 922 925

19. Iron Bridge, North Street, Exeter

♣

In 1833 the Exeter Commissioners of Improvement had responsibility for the maintenance of North Street to St David's Hill, Exeter, the commencement of the Barnstaple road. To reduce the gradients down to the crossing of the Longbrook they considered retaining walls filled with rubble and also masonry arches. However, by March 1834 a contract had been placed with Messrs Russell and Brown of Worcester for a cast-iron structure with masonry approaches to be built by Thomas Whitaker, who became County Surveyor in 1842. A sum of £6500 would be provided by the Improvement Commissioners and £2500 by the Exeter Turnpike Trust. The cast-iron work, costing about £3000, was fabricated at the Blaina Ironworks and shipped to Exeter Basin from Newport. The bridge was substantially completed by July 1835 with the approaches completed in 1836.

The bridge has six 40 ft spans, is 26 ft wide and falls at a 1 in 20 gradient to the north-west. Each span has six arch ribs in two pieces, carrying cross girders surmounted by plates as decking, all in cast iron. The six arch ribs are carried at their springings by a cross girder supported by three cast-iron columns. The balustrading has ornamental verticals with a top rail. The masonry approaches are

HEW 981

SX 917 927

Iron Bridge, North Street, Exeter

160 ft long at the south-eastern end with a 1 in 17 gradient and 350 ft long at the north-western end with a 1 in 20 gradient. They are part masonry arches, now fitted with doors and letout, and part fill between masonry walls.

In 1909 concrete decking was placed over the plates which was replaced in 1984–85 by a reinforced concrete deck. A weight restriction of 3 tons and a vehicle width of 6 ft 6 in. applies to the viaduct roadway. It is Listed Grade II.

20. The Underground Passages, Exeter

◆

HEW 1175

**SX 926 935 to
SX 923 928**

The Underground Passages[1] is a collective name given to a system of man-made tunnels beneath central Exeter which for many centuries served as the city's most important water source. The tunnels were driven by the Cathedral and City authorities and led from wells and springs at the head of the Longbrook valley around 600 yd to the north-east of the old city. They were necessary to achieve a gravity feed because a ridge of volcanic rock lay between the city and the wells, particularly near the Eastgate.

In 1226 the Cathedral granted to St Nicholas Priory one third of the water from the well of St Sidwell, a source abandoned in the fourteenth century. Around 1348 the Cathedral drove a new water conduit from the Cathedral Well but this was cut in 1857 by the construction of the London and South Western Railway. An inadequate supply was maintained from this source by the use of an hydraulic ram until the early 1900s. The City drew on their own nearby well from 1420. This was used until about 1836–7, when it was replaced by a piped supply from the river Exe via Danes Castle reservoir, the source used today. The passages, typically 7 ft 6 in. wide are open to the public in the summer with a specially built entrance off the High Street towards Northernhay Place.

1. MINCHINTON W. *Life in the City*. Devon Books, Exeter, 1987, 4–21.

21. Reinforced Concrete Church, Exeter

♣

HEW 1496

SX 926 930

Reinforced concrete as a structural material was introduced from France towards the end of the nineteenth century. Many methods of combining steel and concrete were patented and promoted. They were summarised by a report to the Institution of Civil Engineers in 1910 which described British Patents of Coignet (1855), Monier (1883) and Hennebique (1892).[1] Other systems included that of Paul Cottancin who designed the Methodist Church in Sidwell Street.[2]

The church, built between 1902 and 1907, is a combination of reinforced concrete and reinforced brickwork. A cellular slab foundation, filled with earth, supports a 70 ft square red brick wall of two 3 in. special cored brick skins with a 20 in. cavity joined by reinforced diaphragms all extending the full height to the underside of the dome. There is a 13 ft wide gallery cantilevered from three walls. It comprises two sloping thin reinforced concrete slabs integral with a system of web members. Under a 105 tons test load it deflected only ⅜ in.[3]

The octagonally domed roof has an inner skin of reinforced brick work and an outer layer of 2 in. thick rein-

Reinforced
Concrete
Church, Exeter

forced concrete. At the apex there is a lantern and venti-
lating turret. The elaborate decorative mouldings around
the doors and windows resemble stonework but are actually of reinforced concrete.

1. *Preliminary and interim report of the committee on reinforced concrete.*
Instn Civ. Engrs, London, 1910.

2. Howard M. Cottancin and an Exeter church. *Concrete*, Cement and
Concrete Association, 1977, 11, Jan., 24–27.

3. Edgell G. J. The remarkable structures of Paul Cottancin. *Struct.
Engnr, 1985*, **63A**, July, 201–204.

22. Cowley Bridge

This three-span ashlar masonry arch bridge[1] is typical of the larger bridges designed by James Green. It was built between 1813 and 1814, only five years after Green's appointment as Devon's first County Bridge Surveyor, a post which he held from 1808 to 1841. The bridge spans the river Creedy but it is also in the flood plain of the River Exe, a branch of which connected upstream to the Creedy.

HEW 997

SX 907 955

From 1851 until 1976 the Exe's flood plain was partially blocked by the Exeter to Crediton railway. Then works by the South West Water Authority and British Rail allowed a direct channel to be built from the Exe to the Creedy immediately upstream of the bridge, which greatly improved the flow through the bridge. The spans are 50 ft, 55 ft and 50 ft and the width between parapets 22 ft 3 in. There is a dentillated string course.

It was Green's most expensive single bridge; the cost of £9000 was shared equally between the County of Devon and the City of Exeter. It now carries the A377 primary route from Exeter to Barnstaple and is a Scheduled Ancient Monument.

1. HENDERSON C. and JERVOISE E. *Old Devon bridges*. Wheaton, Exeter, 1938, 60–1.

Cowley Bridge

♣

23. Thorverton Bridge

HEW 1087

SS 936 016

Above:
Thorverton
Bridge

This single-span early reinforced concrete road bridge[1] is the only road crossing over the River Exe in the 10 miles between Cowley and Bickleigh. It comprises four reinforced concrete arch ribs of 84 ft span and 6 ft rise, spaced at 6 ft centres. The ribs, of section 15 in. by 30 in., carry a cantilevered reinforced concrete deck between reinforced concrete parapets.

In May 1907 the Northern County Surveyor, S. Ingram, submitted plans and an estimate of £1750 for the bridge and approaches. Nine tenders were received of which three were for an alternative design by the Consulting Engineers, L. G. Mouchel, and one a design, by the Indented Bar Company. The lowest tender, to the County Surveyor's design, was accepted from H. Berry of Crediton in the sum of £1630. The bridge was opened on 1 December 1908 for a final cost of £2392. It was load tested to 66 tons which caused the middle two arch ribs to deflect 3/32 in. at the centre of the span and the two outer ribs to deflect 1/16 in.

1. HENDERSON C. and JERVOISE E. *Old Devon bridges.* Wheaton, Exeter, 1938, 53–4.

24. The Grand Western Canal and Halberton Aqueduct

John Rennie surveyed a canal route from the River Exe at Topsham to the River Tone at Taunton and an Act was subsequently obtained in 1796. Work did not proceed immediately and it was not until between 1810 and 1814 that a short length of main canal at Holcombe Rogus and the Tiverton branch were constructed to convey limestone to Tiverton. This length was at one level and remained in use until 1925.

A further length of canal from the Devon–Somerset border at Holcombe Rogus to Taunton was constructed from June 1831 by James Green. Considerable difficulties were experienced in making the inclined plane at Wellisford work satisfactorily and in overcoming faults with the vertical lifts.[1] Green was dismissed in February 1836 but this section of canal was completed on 28 June 1838.

By 1844 the Bristol and Exeter Railway (HEW 1072, p.105) was opened and this was followed by a branch line from Tiverton Junction at Willand to Tiverton on 12 June 1848. To enable the line to be built, I. K. Brunel constructed an aqueduct for the canal at Halberton[2,3] of two

The Grand Western Canal:
HEW 1081
SS 963 124 to
ST 073 196

Halberton Aqueduct:
HEW 523
SS 997 122

Halberton
Aqueduct

brick arches carrying an iron trough manufactured by Kerslake of Exeter. In later years extensive leakage damaged the brickwork and in 1976 the lining was reinforced by butyl rubber. The surfaces of the towpath were waterproofed and much of the brick facing replaced. Later the timber post and rail fence was removed and replaced by a brick parapet.

In 1867 railway competition closed the canal's Somerset section, the plane and lifts were dismantled and most of the earthworks have now disappeared, though they can be traced with the aid of the 1/25 000 map ST 02/12 Wellington. The canal in Devon is now a Country Park. There are no locks, but there are 17 highway bridges and the aqueduct at Halberton to maintain.

1. GREEN J. The canal lifts on the Grand Western Canal. *Trans. Instn Civ. Engrs*, 1838, **2**, 185–191.

2. HARRIS H. *The Grand Western Canal*. David and Charles, Newton Abbot, 1973, 169.

3. THOMAS D. St J. *West country railway history*. David and Charles, Newton Abbot, 1973, 46.

25. St Saviour's Bridge, Ottery St Mary

♣

HEW 947

SY 094 951

This cast-iron single-span arch bridge over the River Otter at Ottery St Mary was built in 1851[1] and is a Scheduled Ancient Monument. It lies downstream of four three-arch masonry or brick bridges by James Green and upstream of two more built by him. There has been a bridge on the site since 1355. It has five 83 ft span arched ribs spaced at 5 ft centres, the segmental arched ribs being of I-section, 2 ft 5 in. deep with 8 in. wide flanges. The ribs support cast-iron trays to carry the road surface with cast-iron railings above the outer girders.

At the centre of the span on each side is a cast-iron plate inscribed 'Built by Joseph Butler and Company, Stanningly Ironworks, near Leeds 1851'. In form of construction the bridge, now a Scheduled Ancient Monument resembles the railway bridges at Thornhill near Dewsbury, Yorkshire, built by the same firm in 1847.[2]

In 1992 the Devon County Council widened this bridge by extending the abutments, moving the southern

St Saviour's Bridge

arch rib and inserting six universal beams betweeen the arch ribs to carry a new reinforced concrete deck with new parapets just inside the original ones.

1. HENDERSON C. and JERVOISE E. *Old Devon Bridges*. Wheaton, Exeter, 1938, 73–4.

2. BARBEY M. F. *Civil engineering heritage: northern England*. Thomas Telford, London, 1981, 106.

26. Axmouth Bridge, Seaton

♣

HEW 615

SY 253 900

This is one of Britain's oldest unreinforced concrete bridges. It was designed by Philip Brannon and was built in 1877 for the Axmouth Bridge Undertaking as a toll bridge.[1] It carries the B3172 Axmouth road over the River Axe, near the river's mouth on the eastern approach to Seaton. The bridge has three spans, the centre is 50 ft with a 7 ft 6 in. rise and the side spans 30 ft with 5 ft 6 in. rises. The width overall is 24 ft giving 21 ft between the parapets.

The arch faces are scored to imitate voussoirs but the construction joint between the arch and the spandrel is clearly visible. During construction, the pier on the Seaton side of the river settled about 2 ft causing the main

Axmouth Bridge

arch to crack across the bridge's full width. In 1956 the centre span was relieved of traffic by the provision of a timber deck, carried on steel girders, supported above the piers. The consequent raising of the deck meant that the parapets also had to be raised which was done by timber handrailing infilled with wire netting.

At one time, the owners, Devon County Council, expected to demolish this bridge and replace it with a modern structure. However in 1978 the bridge was Scheduled as an Ancient Monument and a new upstream bridge was built between 1989–90 leaving the original for pedestrians.

1. STANLEY C. C. *Highlights in the history of concrete*. Cement and Concrete Association, Wexham Springs, 1979, 21.

HEW 592

SY 317 924

27. Cannington Viaduct

This is the only substantial structure on the Axminster to Lyme Regis branch light railway, which operated from 1903 and was managed by the London and South Western Railway. Designed by A. C. Pain and built by Baldry and Yerbergh of Westminster using an overhead cableway, the viaduct has ten arches faced with precast con-

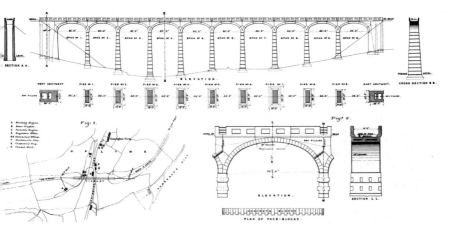

Cannington
Viaduct

crete voussoirs. The remainder of the arches and the piers are constructed in mass concrete, with lime mortar expansion joints.[1] The elliptical arches span 50 ft, are 16 ft wide and are of 92 ft maximum height. The single line was on a gradient of 1 in 80 and the length of the viaduct is 203 yd. The piers taper with 2 in. offsets at the construction joints. As with the Axmouth bridge (HEW 615), one pier settled after construction, so the third arch from the Axminster end has a supporting brick arch within. Cement for the concrete came in by sea to the Cobb at Lyme Regis (HEW 414, p.137) and flint for the aggregate from the cuttings nearby.

The line was closed by British Rail in 1965. Since then various attempts have been made to revive the route, first as a narrow gauge railway, then as a long distance footpath but without success.

1. WOOD-HILL A. and PAIN E. D. On the construction of a concrete railway- viaduct. *Proc. Instn Civ. Engrs.* 1904, **160**, 1–61.

1. Dulverton and Landacre Bridges
2. Tarr Steps
3. New Bridge, Allerford
4. Town Bridges, Bridgwater
5. Bridgwater Dock
6. Somerset Levels
7. Neolithic Trackways
8. Burrow Bridge
9. Langport Bridge
10. Chard Canal
11. Bristol and Exeter Railway
12. Great Western Railway, Reading to Taunton
13. Frome Station Roof
14. Charlton Viaduct
15. Foss Way
16. Town Bridge, Bradford-on-Avon
17. Garden Lake Dam, Stourhead

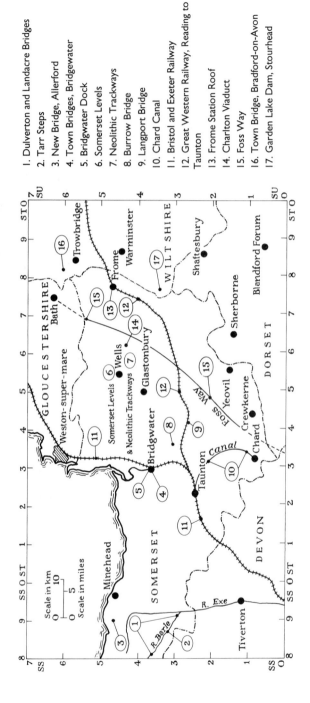

4. Somerset and Mid-Wiltshire

The area has a substantial coastline which forms part of the southern side of the Bristol Channel. The only harbour of note within this length is about 15 miles up the River Parrett's estuary at Bridgwater where the distinctive high tidal range, of some 30 ft, influenced the design of the quay works. These included an inner non-tidal basin which connected to the Bridgwater and Taunton Canal. The canal age is further illustrated by the Chard Canal which extended the former canal to Chard and required the construction of tunnels, locks and inclined planes. It was completed in 1842 and was the last major English canal work until the Manchester Ship Canal in 1894.

Only a few years after the opening of the Chard Canal, through trains were running from London to Exeter via the Great Western (GWR) and the Bristol and Exeter (BER) Railways. As well as providing branch lines, subsequent works were directed towards shortening this route which was only finally achieved in 1906. This enabled the GWR to compete more effectively with the London and South Western Railway. A number of important works were made necessary by Brunel's BER route, including Somerset Bridge over the River Parrett, the Whiteball Tunnel and New Cut Bridge, a road bridge which was associated with Brunel's river training works on the Tone. Frome station, built in 1850, originally for the Wilts, Somerset and Weymouth Railway, has one of the earliest timber roofs still in use and other significant railway works included the impressive 27-arch Charlton Viaduct at Shepton Mallett.

Significant foot and road bridges include the 17-span Tarr Steps clapper bridge over the River Barle and the well known nine-span masonry bridge at Bradford-on-Avon, which are both believed to be of medieval origin. Later masonry work is typified by Burrow Bridge which was built to improve navigation on the River Parrett in 1825. The use of wrought iron is illustrated by the Town Bridge at Bridgwater which was constructed in the 1880s.

A substantial low lying area of some 200 sq. miles between the Bristol Avon to the north and the Quantock Hills to the south is known as the

Somerset Levels. Efforts to drain and to control the flow of water within this area have continued through the centuries. Within this area significant evidence has been uncovered of numerous Neolithic trackways. The Sweet Track, which is the oldest and one of the more recently discovered, is thought to date from around 4000 BC. Of somewhat less antiquity the Roman Foss Way traversed the area from its start near to Seaton on the Devon coast to its ultimate destination at Lincoln. Remains of its agger, or embankment, are visible near Shepton Mallett and Radstock.

Most civil engineering work is associated with commercial or industrial activity. Exceptions are found in the grounds of the National Trust's Stourhead property where three dams were built in the mid-eighteenth century to retain ornamental lakes, one of which has an area of 20 acres.

Dulverton Bridge

1. Dulverton Bridge and Landacre Bridge

From its source on the heights of Exmoor over 1400 ft above sea-level, the River Barle flows south-easterly for about 25 miles through some of the National Park's finest scenery, to join the River Exe near Exebridge on the Somerset–Devon border.

At Dulverton, 2 miles above the confluence, the Barle is crossed by a masonry bridge of five pointed arches, carrying the Dulverton to Exebridge road, B3222. Probably medieval in origin, the arches, spanning 14 ft and rising 5 ft, show double rings on the downstream side and single upstream. In 1819 the bridge was widened by 5 ft on the upstream side, to give an overall width of 17 ft 6 in. A stone plaque in the upstream parapet records that this work was carried out by John Stone of Yarcombe, Devon, and an adjacent plaque records repairs in 1684. The 5 ft wide piers have triangular cutwaters at each end.

Another masonry bridge of five pointed arches carries a minor road between Exford and North Molton over the

Dulverton Bridge :
HEW 1726
SS 912 278

Landacre Bridge:
HEW 1727
SS 816 361

Landacre Bridge

river Barle at Landacre. The spans are 9 ft, with a rise of 3 ft, and show a double ring on both elevations. There are triangular cutwaters at each end of the 4 ft wide piers. Unlike Dulverton Bridge, this bridge has not been widened; it has an overall width of 11 ft 6 in.

Repairs to Landacre Bridge are recorded in the Somerset County archives from at least 1621; substantial repairs were carried out in 1828 by John Brewer, a Dulverton mason.[1]

1. GREENFIELD D. J. Some Exmoor bridges. *Exmoor Review*, Dulverton, 1987, 27–28.

♣

HEW 863

SS 868 321

2. Tarr Steps, Exmoor

Tarr Steps is a seventeen-span clapper bridge, 130 ft long, over the River Barle 4 miles north-west of Dulverton; a minor road between Winsford and Hawkridge fords the river alongside.

Unhewn stone slabs, the clappers, 7 to 10 in. thick and up to 10 ft long and 5 ft wide, rest on unmortared stone piers, about 9 ft long by 3 ft wide by 3 ft high. Raking slabs upstream and downstream of each pier break the

Tarr Steps, Exmoor

force of the river when in spate and divert debris over the clappers.

The construction is typical of clapper bridges, Tarr Steps differing from several on Dartmoor only by the large number of spans and the raking slabs.

The bridge, reputedly medieval, was demolished by floods in 1952; fortunately a survey had been made in 1949 following earlier damage and the owners, Somerset County Council, were able to replace the clappers in their original positions.

3. New Bridge, Allerford

♣

To the north of Dunkery Beacon (SS 891 416), the highest point on Exmoor at 1704 ft above sea-level, the moors and woods are drained by short but very steep streams which unite to form Horner Water before entering Porlock Bay. The Porlock to Minehead road A39 crosses Horner Water on an unusual masonry bridge. New Bridge, so called from at least the early seventeenth century, consists of a high, pointed arch spanning 18 ft and rising 8 ft, with a 4 ft

HEW 1728

SS 900 466

New Bridge, Allerford

span half-arch on each side of the main arch for flood relief. Originally 12 ft 6 in. wide overall, 6 ft was added on the downstream side in 1866 by Dunster Highway Board,[1] in the same style as the original, except that the newer section shows a single arch ring on the elevation rather than the older double ring.

1. GREENFIELD D. J. Some Exmoor bridges. *Exmoor Review*, Dulverton, 1987, 29.

4. Town Bridges, Bridgwater

♣

HEW 1520

HEW 1519

ST 300 370

Town Bridge, Bridgwater, cast-iron bridge, 1797–1833

In the centre of Bridgwater the River Parrett is crossed by a 75 ft span wrought iron road bridge, with seven latticed arch ribs of 7 ft 3 in. rise.[1] The width between cast-iron parapets is 36 ft. Built in 1883, it was, until 1958, the town's only road crossing of the River Parrett. The design, by R. C. Else and G. B. Laffan, is unusual. There are T-section top and bottom arch rib booms with diagonal crossed channel web members on alternate sides.

The bridge is partly supported by the abutments of the earliest cast-iron bridge in Somerset, completed in 1797. This had an elliptical arch of 75 ft span, 23 ft rise, with five

ribs in the width of 24 ft including footways. Each outer rib had spandrel infilling of diminishing circles and a complex design of curved members next to the abutments. The ribs were cast in sections at Coalbrookdale by Thomas Gregory, who had been responsible for the ironwork of the Ironbridge (HEW 136).[2]

The tall slender parapet railings had ornamental panels at the centre, surmounted by oil lamps. There was an earlier masonry arch bridge reputed to date from the twelfth century.

1. MURLESS B. J. *Bridgwater docks and the River Parrett*. Somerset County Library, 1983, 5–6.

2. SIVEWRIGHT W. J. *Civil engineering heritage: Wales and western England*. Thomas Telford, London, 1986, 169.

5. Bridgwater Dock ♣

HEW 632

ST 297 375

In the eighteenth and nineteenth centuries, schemes were devised to enable shipping to cope with the River Parrett's 30 ft tidal range, which made river quays dangerous and inconvenient. The solution was Bridgwater Dock, opened in 1841 two months before the Bristol and Exeter Railway (HEW 1072) reached the town.

A half acre half-tide basin on the west bank, 500 yd downstream of Town Bridge (HEW 1520), was constructed with access from the river by a pair of lock gates 40 ft wide and a 14 ft wide barge lock. This basin is connected to an inner basin called the 'Floating Dock' because it is non-tidal. There are two pairs of mitre gates to maintain a constant water level in the inner basin whatever the level in the tidal basin, enabling ships up to 600 tons to pass into the inner basin, which is about 600 ft by 200 ft. From the north-west corner a lock connects to the Bridgwater and Taunton Canal. Thomas Maddicks supervised construction of the dock; Chapple was the Contractor.[1]

The Parrett carries large quantities of silt. To remove it from the tidal basin, scouring culverts were provided to make use of water from the inner basin but these were found to be inadequate. A steam drag-boat or scraper (HEW 1145, p.74), designed by I. K. Brunel, was purchased in 1845 and worked continuously almost until the dock closed in 1971.

Bridgwater Docks, Bascule Bridge and warehouses

A double-leaf bascule bridge (HEW 1526 ST 298 375), built in 1841, originally of cast iron, carries Chilton Road over the cut between the basins. The present bridge is of mild steel and dates from 1907; it was overhauled in 1983 and can now be operated electrically.

The inner basin is currently used as a marina, with residential and commercial accommodation in and around the 1841 four-storey red brick warehouse.

In 1863 the Bristol and Exeter Railway Company (BER) acquired from Bridgwater Corporation a 4 ft 8½ in. gauge tramway, which was laid in 1845 from the railway station to an east bank wharf. The spur was made mixed gauge in 1867 to take the Company's vehicles, and carried over the river to the west dock system which the BER had acquired. As the river was navigable, the railway bridge had to open. Francis Fox, Engineer to the BER, designed a wrought iron plate girder telescopic bridge (HEW 1106, ST 300 374) at a 30° skew to the river. This was built by Warburton Brothers of Bristol, the ironwork being fabricated by Lloyds Foster and Company of Wednesbury.

The western span, 65 ft 9 in. long, is fixed, its eastern end is supported on two 6 ft diameter cast iron columns. The columns also support, by skids, the western ends of the two movable 127 ft 3 in. long main girders, which are at 15 ft 6 in. centres and 6 ft 2 in. deep. These rest on rollers at the east abutment and at their eastern ends. Their river opening span is 78 ft. The next 80 ft of track eastwards was supported on girders mounted on transverse wheels, so that this section could be traversed sideways to allow the main girders to be retracted eastwards.[2] When the bridge came into use in 1871, hand operation was used, but replaced by steam the same year. The bridge last opened in 1953. In 1974 British Rail demolished the traverser section but, following public protest, the bridge was Scheduled as an Ancient Monument. Now it is owned by Somerset County Council who incorporated it as a fixed bridge in the town road system until the completion in 1988 of Chandos Bridge alongside. The timber deck was replaced by concrete without altering outward appearances. The boiler from the steam engine was removed to Westonzoyland Pumping Station (HEW 1409 ST 338 329) for preservation in 1977.

1. MURLESS B. J. *Bridgwater Docks and the River Parrett*. Somerset County Library, 1983, 12–20.

2. FISH R. J. The telescopic railway bridge at Bridgwater, Somerset. *Journal Historical Model Railway Society.*, 1983, 2, 175–177.

6. The Somerset Levels

♠

For many people the Somerset Levels are epitomised by Sedgemoor, scene of the battle (ST 351 355) in 1685 when the Duke of Monmouth and his followers were defeated. In fact the Levels and Moors comprise over 200 sq. miles of land lying below mean high water, from the Bristol Avon in the north to the Quantock Hills in the south.[1,2]

HEW 1407

ST 30 60 to 50 60

ST 20 20 to 50 20

The area of greatest engineering activity lies between the Mendip Hills and the River Parrett, reaching up to 15 miles inland from the Severn estuary. Ridges running east to west from the inland uplands, which contribute another 800 sq. miles to the catchment area, divide this area broadly into the basins of the Rivers Axe, Brue, Huntspill, King's Sedgemoor Drain and Parrett and their

Somerset Levels, Kings Sedgemoor Drain with regulating sluice, looking westwards from adjacent Greylake Bridge

tributaries. The moors, which are mainly peat, are separated from the coast by a marginally higher clay belt about 6 miles wide, forming a barrier to natural drainage. In addition, the tidal range of over 40 ft prevents the rivers from discharging when tide-locked. In the past, when bank-full rivers were penned back by high tides at times of heavy rainfall, disastrous floods frequently occurred. The often conflicting interests of river navigation compounded the problem.

Until the Dissolution of the Monasteries in the 1530s, the great ecclesiastical establishments of Athelney (ST 34 29), Muchelney (ST 42 24), Glastonbury and Wells drained their lands, built sea walls and ciyses (sluices) and constructed embanked causeways linking the drier 'islands'. During the next 200 years further piecemeal improvements were made. However, the characteristic landscape of the levels and moors today — fields divided one from another not by hedges but by 'rhynes' (ditches) linking to arterial waterways — is largely the product of eighteenth and early nineteenth century Enclosure and Drainage Acts.

The first major artificial channel, the King's Sedgemoor Drain, was cut for 12½ miles from the River Cary at ST 435 327 to a clyse into the Parrett at Dunball (ST 310 408). It was completed in 1795. William Jessop advised on this scheme, and designed improvements which were carried out in the basins of the Brue between 1801–6 and the Axe from 1804–10.[3] Robert Anstice of Bridgwater, later to become Somerset's first County Surveyor, was the Resident Engineer for all these schemes and continued in full charge after 1805.[4]

The first steam drainage in the Levels was installed in the early 1830s near Westonzoyland (HEW 1409 ST 338 329);[5] a small beam engine coupled to a scoop wheel lifted water from the rhynes draining Weston Level to the Parrett. In 1861 this was replaced by a steam-driven drainage machine which was manufactured by Easton, Amos and Sons and incorporated an Appold centrifugal pump. By 1869 seven more of these pumping units were installed at stations built by local Drainage Boards.[6] Between 1948 and 1955 all steam stations were abandoned or replaced by diesel, but five of these engines were preserved; that at Westonzoyland has been restored by a Trust, who regularly exhibit it in steam and who are

Seymour sea-wall, Somerset Levels

developing the station as a museum of land drainage. The first electric pump was installed in 1963 and all diesels have been replaced.

Entering the Parrett estuary through a clyse at ST 293 457 is the 5½ mile long Huntspill River, 17 ft deep and up to 60 ft wide. Constructed between 1938 and 1944, it serves both as a flood relief channel for the Brue and as a reservoir for a large ordnance factory. Excavation problems through the clay belt were the subject of an early soil mechanics study.[7]

The Parrett Flood Relief Scheme was complete in 1972 at a cost of £1 400 000. A 7½ mile long embanked channel known as the Sowy River was cut from the Parrett near Langport (ST 409 276) to the King's Sedgemoor Drain (ST 379 351), which was widened and regraded. Dunball Clyse was rebuilt, embodying a fresh water seal between lifting gates to prevent salt water entering the Drain; in wet months the gates are raised and the land water discharges through tidal flaps. In 1974 a similar clyse was completed at Brean Cross (HEW 1408 ST 308 562) forming the tidal limit of the Axe, about 1¾ miles upstream of the Severn estuary.

Flooding in the levels and moors has not been entirely eliminated, but the agricultural improvements achieved so far are raising fears among conservationists about the future of the last remaining wetlands in the West Country.

1. WILLIAMS M. *The draining of the Somerset Levels*. Cambridge University Press, 1970.

2. KELTING E. L. *An outline of the development of main drainage in Somerset*. Paper for a party from the International Commission on land Drainage, Whitby Light and Lane, Bridgwater, 1971.

3. HADFIELD C. and SKEMPTON A. W. *William Jessop, Engineer*. David and Charles, Newton Abbot, 1979, 84–8, 248.

4. BENTLEY J. B. Robert Anstice — Somerset's first County Surveyor. *Bulletin, Somerset Industrial Archaeological Society*, 1987, 46, 10–15.

5. MILES I. *Bogs and inundations*. Somerset Industrial Archaeological Society and Westonzoyland Engine Trust, Taunton, 1993, 17–25.

6. WATKINS G. *The steam engine in industry - the public services*. Moorland Publishing, London, 1978, 95–102.

7. COOLING L. F. Soil mechanics and site exploration. *Proc. Instn Civ. Engrs*, 1941, **18**, 59–61.

7. Neolithic trackways, Somerset Levels ♠

HEW 920

ST 38 45 to ST 47 45

ST 38 40 to ST 47 40

Peat digging in the Somerset Levels north of the Polden Hills, especially during the large scale activities of the past few decades, has revealed that some 15 sq. miles of peat moors near Meare, the site of Iron Age lake villages (ST 445 422), were crossed by numerous Neolithic trackways. Since the early 1970s the Universities of Cambridge and Exeter have been researching the trackways,[1] which have been well preserved by the waterlogged peat and shown by radio-carbon dating to have varying ages between 4000 and 6000 years old.

In about 1835 a stretch of corduroy trackway was discovered. Subsequent excavations showed it to have run for 1½ miles between the 'islands' of Burtle (ST 402 430) and Westhay (ST 435 422). Fancifully christened 'The Abbot's Way', the track, dating from about 2500 BC, is some 4 ft wide, of split alder logs laid transversely. Pegs were driven at the sides either for setting-out or as guides and in some cases longitudinal stringers were bound to the pegs and to the ends of the transverse members by withy ties.

Another type of track, dating from about 3000 BC, has been found on Walton Heath (ST 45 39), 3 miles west of Glastonbury. This is of woven hurdle construction in panels about 8 ft long and 3 ft 6 in. wide. The 1 in. diameter cross members are spaced at about 2 ft centres; the longitudinal members, about ¾ in. diameter, are closely woven under and over them. Withy ropes tie the members together and to pegs driven alongside for alignment. In places there are as many as five layers of hurdles, presumably resulting from maintenance work.

The oldest trackway (about 4000 BC) is the 1 mile long Sweet Track (ST 429 417 to ST 422 402), named after the peat-cutter who first uncovered it in 1970. Although no more than a narrow cat-walk, running south from Westhay towards the Poldens, its structure is surprisingly sophisticated and suggests a well-planned and organised approach to the problem of crossing the marsh, using standardised components. Longitudinal log rails, up to 20 ft long and 3 in. diameter, were laid along the centre line. Pairs of pegs about 3 in. in diameter and 3 ft long were driven straddling the rail to form an 'X', in the upper part of which were laid split planks, mostly oak, up to 10 ft long and 2 ft wide. These were given additional support by peat packing and occasional pegs on the heads of which the planks rested. Additional stability came from pegs driven through holes in the planks and notches in their ends. The work was a remarkable achievement for a time when the only tools for felling and fabrication were of stone or wood.

By arrangement with the landowners and peat-cutters, 70 ft of the Abbot's Way is being kept undisturbed under several feet of peat in the vicinity of ST 410 425, and 100 ft of Sweet Track at ST 423 404. It is hoped that in the course of time preservation techniques will have advanced to the point where these relics can be displayed *in situ*. A panel of hurdle track, preserved by a wax process, is displayed in the Castle Museum, Taunton, with elements of the Sweet Track. The Tribunal Museum, Glastonbury, has a piece of the Sweet Track planking, a few artefacts and photographs of the excavations. Short lengths of each type of trackway have been reconstructed at the Somerset Levels Museum, Shapwick Road, Westhay.

1. COLES B. and J. *Sweet Track to Glastonbury — the Somerset Levels in prehistory.* Thames and Hudson, London, 1986.

Below: Burrow Bridge

8. Burrow Bridge

♣

Burrow Bridge was rebuilt in 1825 to improve navigation on the River Parrett, replacing a 200 year old three-span masonry structure. The new bridge has one 68 ft span segmental arch, a 14 ft rise, and is said to be the longest masonry span carrying a road over a river in Somerset. It carries the A361 road from Taunton to Glastonbury.

HEW 1518

ST 358 304

The spandrels are pierced, and both these 'flood tunnels' and the arch voussoirs are of granite, the remaining masonry being lias limestone.

The bridge was built to the general design of Philip Ilett of Taunton by John Stone of Yarcombe, Devon, whose family built many bridges in Somerset in the early nineteenth century.

9. Langport Bridge

♣

This handsome three-span lias limestone arch bridge, also known as Great Bow Bridge, carrying the A378 Langport to Taunton road, was built by the Parrett Navigation Company in 1840–41, with other works aimed at improving river navigation.[1] The 28 ft outer spans have a 5 ft 7 in. rise and the centre 34 ft span a rise of 6 ft 9 in. All are semi-elliptical. Piers are 6 ft wide and the width between parapets 24 ft. Under the Navigation Compa-

HEW 1509

ST 415 266

Langport Bridge

ny's Act of 1836, I. K. Brunel became their Consulting Engineer. William Gravatt, his assistant, designed the bridge while supervising construction of the Bristol and Exeter Railway (HEW 1072). Edwin Down of Bridgwater was the Contractor.

The bridge replaced nine spans of a medieval bridge, described in 1616 as having 'one and thirty bowes', or arches.[2] In 1987 ground-probing radar techniques revealed nineteen remaining arches under 'Bow Street', the ¼ mile long causeway carrying the A378 between Great and Little Bow Bridge (ST 419 268).

1. HADFIELD C. *The canals of south-west England*. David & Charles, Newton Abbot, 1967, 83–91.

2. ROSS REV. D. MELVILLE. The Papers of the former Corporation of Langport, 1596–1886. *Proc. Somerset Archaeological & Natural History Society*, 1907, 53, 164.

♠

HEW 1345

**ST 271 256 to
ST 329 093**

10. Chard Canal

James Green's original design for the 13½ mile long Chard Canal was extensively modified by Sydney Hall, the young Engineer employed by the Canal Company on the recommendation of William Cubitt.[1] Hall overcame the 231 ft level difference between its junction with the Bridgwater and Taunton Canal, at Creech St Michael and Chard Basin by constructing a lock and four innovatory inclined planes. Three tunnels pierced intervening ridges and a 50 acre reservoir near Chard supplied water to the canal. It was completed in 1842, the last English 'mainline' canal until the Manchester Ship Canal (HEW 88)[2] opened in 1894. Three of the inclines at Thornfalcon, Wrantage and Ilminster were double-tracked and counterbalanced, the tub-boats 26 ft by 6 ft 6 in. being carried afloat in caissons, probably the first time that this method had been used.[3] Motion was produced by adding extra water to the upper caisson. The fourth, at Chard Common (ST 337 103), was unique in Britain, being single-track and powered by a water turbine with a 25 ft head.[4] Boats were raised 86 ft in a wheeled cradle up a slope of 1 in 10.

The canal was abandoned in 1867. Little trace of the inclined planes now remains. Chard Reservoir continues as a prominent beauty spot, the crest of its dam carries a minor road from Chard to Chaffcombe. Best preserved of the tunnel remains is the north portal of the 1 mile 90 yd long Crimson Hill Tunnel (HEW 1473, ST 311 221).

1. HADFIELD C. *The Canals of south-west England.* David and Charles, Newton Abbot, 1967, 67.

2. BARBEY M. F. *Civil engineering heritage: northern England.* Thomas Telford, London, 1981, 164–165.

3. HADFIELD C. The evolution of the canal inclined plane. *Journal Railway & Canal Historical Society,* 1979, **25**, 3, 98.

4. HADFIELD C. Op cit., 71.

11. Bristol and Exeter Railway

The Bristol and Exeter Railway (BER) was built contemporaneously with the Great Western Railway (HEW 1071),[1] of which it was virtually an extension. It did much towards opening up the south-western peninsula of Britain.

HEW 1072

ST 597 724 to SX 919 923

I. K. Brunel, the Engineer for the 77 mile long railway, used his broad gauge. His assistant, William Gravatt, surveyed the route in 1835 and was Resident Engineer during construction between Bristol and Whiteball.[2] William Froude supervised the work onward to Exeter.[3]

Work began in 1836 from Bristol, the line reaching Bridgwater in 1841, Taunton in July 1842 and the first train from London to Exeter ran on 1 May 1844. The 4 hour 40 min. journey back to Paddington was nearly four times as fast as the stage coach.

The BER opened without rolling stock of its own and the route was leased to the Great Western Railway (GWR) until 1849. At Bristol, the terminal station was not built until 1852, but tracks were linked with GWR lines from the beginning. In 1876, the BER was finally taken over by the GWR and the present Temple Meads station (HEW 436)[4] was built to replace both termini.

Two miles south of Weston-super-mare, the route cuts through the western extremity of the Mendip hills at Uphill, where it is crossed by an elegant masonry arch bridge (HEW 1079, ST 327 581). It has an span of 115 ft 6 in., a rise of 17 ft, and is 18 ft 6 in. wide between brick parapets. The edge voussoirs are stepped. The arch crown is 55 ft 9 in. above rail level, the arch springing directly from the rock sides of the cutting. It may be seen from the next bridge to the south, which carries the A370 Weston-super-mare to Bridgwater road.

From Uphill the line runs level and nearly straight across the Somerset Levels (HEW 1407) to Taunton. At the crossing of the River Parrett, just south of Bridgwater (ST 310 355), Brunel built a masonry arch of 100 ft span with only 12 ft rise — half the rise of his famous Thames bridge at Maidenhead (HEW 30, SU 902 810). Unfortunately the foundations moved outwards, so in 1844 he substituted a 102 ft span timber arch, which was in turn replaced by a steel Pratt truss bridge in 1904. This is called Somerset Bridge.

On the appproach to Taunton the line would have crossed a meander in the River Tone, which was then navigable. To avoid two high level bridges close together, Brunel cut a river channel across the meander along the south side of the railway. New Cut Bridge (HEW 1510, ST 250 257) was built to carry the Taunton to Bridgwater road across the new channel. This red brick bridge with sandstone edge voussoirs is the longest span brick arch road bridge in Somerset, spanning 72 ft square and 80 ft skew with a rise of 14 ft. The segmental arch, originally 27 ft wide overall, was widened on the west side in 1933–34 to give 40 ft between parapets by adding a blue brick arch of similar span and rise.

West of Taunton the Blackdown Hills were ascended at gradients of up to 1 in 80 followed by a descent at 1 in 115. At the summit, on the Somerset–Devon border, is the 1092 yd Whiteball Tunnel (HEW 1547, ST 090 180).

From Exeter, the route was continued westwards by the South Devon Railway (HEW 1353, p.68), the first sections of which were opened in 1846.

Another broad gauge line, worked for a time by the BER, was the Exeter and Crediton Railway, from Cowley Bridge Junction (SX 909 954) to Crediton (SX 840 994), which opened in 1851.[5] Eleven years later it was taken over by the London and South Western Railway, and became mixed gauge, including the section between Exeter and Cowley Bridge Junction.

On the BER main line the third rail was added in

Opposite:
Lanport Viaduct
bridge on the
Great Western
Railway

sections, the work being completed in March 1876, shortly after the company had been taken over by the GWR.

1. SIVEWRIGHT W. J. *Civil engineering heritage: Wales and western England.* Thomas Telford, London, 1986, 97.

2. ROLT L. T. C. *Isambard Kingdom Brunel.* Longmans Green, London, 1957, 146.

3. William Froude (obituary memoir) *Min. Proc. Instn Civ. Engrs*, 1880, 60, 396.

4. SIVEWRIGHT W. J. Op cit., 101.

5. MACDERMOTT E. T. and CLINKER, C. R. *History of the Great Western Railway.* 2. Ian Allan, London, 1964, 77–85.

12. Great Western Railway: Reading to Taunton via Castle Cary

HEW 1589

Reading to Taunton via Castle Cary: SU 71 74 to ST 22 25

Having reached Exeter in 1844 by way of the Bristol and Exeter Railway, the Great Western Railway Company (GWR) immediately prepared plans for a more direct route to Exeter. However, it was not until 1906 that this

River Parrett
Bridge on the
Great Western
Railway

was finally achieved, shortening the overall journey from Paddington by 20 miles and enabling the GWR to compete more effectively with the London and South Western Railway, whose shorter line had reached Exeter in 1860.

GWR branch lines provided the nucleus of a Reading to Taunton cut-off. Between 1897 and 1900, 19½ miles of the Berks and Hants line between Hungerford (SU 33 68) and Patney (SU 06 59) were widened and improved and 14½ miles of new line were built from Patney to join the Wilts, Somerset and Weymouth line at Westbury (ST 85 52). Difficult ground conditions around Patney necessitated piling under embankments.

Starting in 1903, a new 15½ mile long line was built from the Weymouth line at Castle Cary (ST 63 33) to Curry Rivel Junction (ST 40 27). Notable engineering works across the hard lias limestone and marl to Langport included a series of deep cuttings and embankments, 'flying' arches over the rock cuttings, a heavily-skewed brick bridge spanning 62 ft over the B3153 Somerton to Castle Cary road (ST 510 292), a high brick viaduct of five

50 ft semicircular arches across the valley of the River Cary (ST 492 292) and a 1056 yd tunnel near Somerton (ST 470 274). From Langport, the line runs for 1 mile across the edge of the Somerset Levels (HEW 1407) to Curry Rivel Junction, crossing the River Parrett by a 105 ft span steel girder bridge with two 40 ft approach spans on each side (ST 415 273). As on the nearby ten-arch brick viaduct of 55 ft spans, the foundations were taken down 50 ft through soft ground to the underlying marl.

At the same time, 4 miles of the Yeovil Branch from Curry Rivel to Athelney (ST 34 29) were raised, widened and strengthened. In addition, a new 3 mile long deviation was built from Athelney to Cogload (ST 31 29), where a junction was made with the Bristol and Exeter Railway.

Avoiding lines were built at Frome and Westbury in 1932 to improve the speed of through expresses.

13. Frome Station Roof ♣

Frome and Newcastle Central (HEW 289)[1] have the earliest through train sheds still in use, opened within a few weeks of one another in 1850. At Frome a 120 ft length of timber roof covers the track and platforms. Twelve composite trusses span 48 ft at 11 ft centres on square timber columns and support timber purlins, which carry patent corrugated roofing panels, with a louvred and glazed clerestory running the ridges full length. Each truss is made up of two inclined timber rafters with horizontal wrought iron ties. Alternate trusses have a wrought iron king tie supporting a spider to which the horizontal ties from adjoining trusses are attached; the diagonal disposition in plan adds longitudinal stability.

HEW 1630

ST 785 476

On the west side, the columns are incorporated into the timber clad walls of the main building. On the east side the rafters project 6 ft beyond the columns to further columns supporting the station's timber side wall, giving the building an assymetrical appearance.

The station was built for the Wilts Somerset and Weymouth Railway, but by the time it was opened on 7 October 1850, the line had already been taken over by the Great Western Railway.

Frome Station

Design was by J. R. Hannaford, one of Brunel's architects. The building is Listed Grade II.

1. BARBEY M. F. *Civil engineering heritage: northern England*. Thomas Telford, London, 1981, 28.

14. Charlton Viaduct, Shepton Mallet

♣

HEW 1508

ST 628 436

The 26 mile long single-line Bath extension of the Somerset and Dorset Railway was opened in 1874 from Evercreech Junction to Bath, with five tunnels and seven large viaducts. Between 1888 and 1894 most of the line was doubled, including the longest viaduct, Charlton, which has 27 segmental arches of 28 ft span.

The original 45 ft high viaduct was built of coursed squared rubble limestone masonry, except for the arch barrels, which are brick. The viaduct is on a curve of 30 chains radius, falling at 1 in 55 from each end to mid-length. Every third pier is buttressed on the outside of the curve and the ninth and eighteenth piers are thickened to resist horizontal forces from the segmental arches.

To accommodate the track doubling, the viaduct was widened by about 15 ft on the inside of the curve. Limestone masonry was again used for the new spandrels, parapet and end-faces of the piers, the arch barrels and the remainder of the widened piers being of brick.

Charlton Viaduct forms an imposing backdrop to the ornamental gardens of industrial premises. The firm bought the structure from British Rail after the line closed in 1966 and has maintained it since, including water-proofing the deck.

Charlton Viaduct

15. Foss Way

♠

HEW 1603

SY 256 898

ST 682 552

This well-known Roman road ran roughly north east from a port in the mouth of the River Axe near Seaton to Lincoln. As far as Dinnington (ST 400 130), there is uncertainty about the route, but north east from there it is traceable throughout, being followed by modern roads and tracks most of the way.

Characteristically, it was laid out as a series of straight alignments. The A303 London to Exeter road follows it from Petherton Bridge (ST 451 167) to Ilchester (Lendiniae) on the River Yeo, where two other Roman roads meet, and there was a Roman wharf. The course is then followed by the A37 road nearly to Shepton Mallet (ST 630 430); a series of tracks and paths and then the A367 Shepton Mallet to Radstock road continues over the Avon County boundary, the alignment leading towards Bath (Aquae Sulis).

Because of continuous use, little original Roman construction survives above ground. The remains of a length of agger, or embankment on which the road was laid, can

Above: Foss Way

Opposite: Town Bridge, Bradford on Avon

be seen near Beacon Farm north of Shepton Mallet (ST 635 449 to ST 636 454), appearing as a low ridge running towards Beacon Hill. Here the route crosses another Roman road from Old Sarum, Wiltshire (SU 13 32), to the Roman mining settlement of Charterhouse (ST 50 55).

At Radstock there is a fine length of agger (ST 680 550 to ST 682 554), 16 ft wide at the base, 8 ft at the top and 3 ft high. A portion was excavated in about 1880, revealing a 3 in. depth of later metalling. Below this, the Roman profile was 6 in. of rubble laid on the subsoil, 2 in. of red marl and pebbles, 18 in. of coarse concrete, 5 in. of fine concrete and 4½ in. of rough stone surface paving.[1]

1. McMurtrie J. The Foss road at Radstock. *Proc. Somerset Archaeological and Natural History Society*, 1884, Part 2, 76.

16. Town Bridge, Bradford-on-Avon

This well-known and much illustrated Scheduled Ancient Monument carries the A363 road over the River Avon in the town centre. Eight of its nine arches have

HEW 1514

ST 826 609

spans between 14 ft 2 in. and 18 ft 3 in. whereas the north-east end arch spans 7 ft 9 in. The overall length is 175 ft.[1]

Originally little more than a packhorse bridge, it was widened on the downstream side with semicircular arches in the seventeenth century to 25 ft 6 in. including footways. On the upstream side, two pointed arches at the south-west end, each with four ribs, are possibly from the thirteenth century. The remaining upstream arches are semicircular with double arch-rings in two orders.

The piers have cutwaters on their upstream ends only. The second pier from the south-west end is wider than the others and its cutwater is corbelled out to support a small square stone building, with a domed roof surmounted by a finial and a copper-gilt weather vane in the shape of a fish (the 'Bradford Gudgeon'). Probably a chapel originally, it served for many years as a lock-up.

There is a second medieval bridge 600 yd downstream, called Barton Bridge. It has four pointed double ring arches in two orders. The width is 11 ft 6 in. between railings which have replaced the original stone parapets. The three piers have massive upstream cutwaters, but none downstream.

1. JERVOISE E. *The ancient bridges of the south of England*. Architectural Press, London, 1930, 118.

17. Garden Lake Dam, Stourhead

♣

HEW 1701

ST 772 338

There are three earth dams in the grounds of the National Trust's Stourhead property. Garden Lake Dam, one of the largest ever built in the mid-eighteenth century, impounds an ornamental lake 20 acres in area. It was under construction in 1754 and reached completion before 1757.[1] The dam has a total length of nearly 1200 ft, comprising a main dam 750 ft long with a maximum height of 23 ft and a branch, the 'Western Arm', 450 ft in length. The inner face, protected by stone pitching, slopes at 3 in 1; the outer slope is about 2 in 1. It is known that the Western Arm has a central core of soft to firm grey clay with a top width of 3 ft and bank fill composed of stony clay.[2] The main dam is doubtless of similar construction. The outfall is through a 12 in. diameter pipe and an

adjustable stop log sluice, augmented after 1953 by a siphon spillway.

Garden Lake Dame, Stourhead

The garden and lake were planned by Henry Flitcroft, architect to Henry Hoare of Stourhead, but whether or not he acted as Engineer for the dam is uncertain.

1. WOODBRIDGE K. *The Stourhead landscape*. National Trust, 1986.

2. Dimensions and other details kindly supplied by Watson Hawksley, consulting engineers.

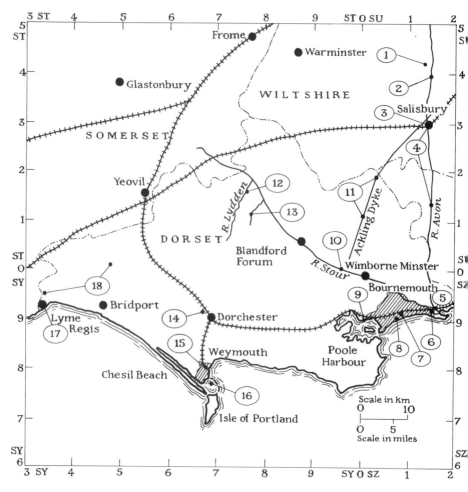

1. Stonehenge

2. Queensberry and Ornamental Bridges, Amesbury

3. Salisbury Cathedral Tower

4. Harnham and Fordingbridge Ancient Bridges

5. Christchurch Ancient Bridge

6. Tuckton Bridge

7. Meyrick Park Water Tower

8. Alum Chine Suspension Bridge

9. Town Cellars, Poole

10. White Mill Bridge, Sturminster Marshall

11. Ackling Dyke

12. Bagber Cast-iron Bridge

13. Fifehead Neville Packhorse Bridge

14. Roman Aqueduct

15. Weymouth Port

16. Portland Harbour

17. Lyme Regis Harbour

18. Charmouth and Beaminster Road Tunnels

5. Dorset and South Wiltshire

Dorset's coastline is very varied in character and its distinctive features include Chesil Beach running for over 20 miles between Bridport and the Isle of Portland which extends several miles into the Channel. The land consequently provided Portland Harbour with natural protection from prevailing south-westerly winds. When enclosed by three breakwaters, to the east, it became the nation's largest artificial harbour. It has continued to develop as a major naval base until recent reductions in defence spending have jeopardised its future in this role. The immediately adjacent Weymouth Harbour and the land-enclosed Poole Harbour, to the east, both provide cross channel ferry links as well as serving local fishing and leisure needs. The latter has the impressive fifteenth century Town Cellars stone building on its waterfront. To the west of Lyme Bay, the Cobb at Lyme Regis is one of Britain's earliest artificial harbours dating from about 1300.

There are several other examples of older engineering works. Salisbury Cathedral, originally dating from the thirteenth century, has required continued attention to preserve the structural integrity of its spire, which is the highest in Britain. Roman engineering is illustrated by the remains of the aqueduct which brought water to Dorchester from the River Frome, some 12 miles distant and Ackling Dyke extended from Old Sarum to the north-east of Wimborne. The oldest work, however, is the impressive, yet enigmatic, stone circle at Stonehenge, dating from the second millenium BC. Both Dorset and South Wiltshire remain predominantly agricultural in character and have experienced relatively little industrial development of substance. There is consequently an absence of major transport development. Canals made little impact in the area and although both the A30 and A303, together with the London and South Western Railway, provide through travel to the West Country, both railways and roads have tended to serve local needs rather than contribute to the nation's principal transport routes. This trend continues to be illustrated by the motorway system, with the M5 and M4 passing well to the area's west and north respectively and the M27 ending at Cadnam to the east of the Dorset–Hampshire boundary..

Several types of masonry bridges are represented, including the three ancient crossings of the River Avon at Harnham, Fordingbridge and Christchurch, together with the White Mill Bridge, Sturminster Marshall, which is believed to be Dorset's oldest, dating from the late twelfth century. There is a cast-iron bridge over the River Lydden, near Sturminster Newton, which displays some ingenious design features, whereas the Tuckton Bridge, over the River Stour at Bournemouth, illustrates an early use of reinforced concrete in bridge building. Also in Bournemouth is found Meyrick Park Water Tower, which was Britain's first to be built of reinforced concrete and a number of bridges over the steep valleys, or chines, running down to the sea which are illustrated by the bridges at Alum Chine.

Road tunnels are not comon in the South of England but two, dating from the early 1830s, are found in south-west Dorset near to Charmouth and Beaminster, cutting through steep greensand scarps.

1. Stonehenge

♣

HEW 248

SU 128 422

The best known megalithic stone circle in the United Kingdom, Stonehenge, stands impressive and mysterious in the rolling landscape of Salisbury Plain. It was built in three main stages between 2800 BC and 1300 BC, the first being earthworks only. The third stage involved the extraordinary feat of bringing eighty 5 ton stones some 240 miles from the Preseli Hills, in South Wales, the nearest source of the igneous rock from which they were hewn. The journey was probably made by water to the nearest point on the River Avon, 1½ miles away. They are no longer in their original positions.

The second stage, about 2100 BC, was the most remarkable. Thirty huge 20-ton sarsen stones were collected from the Marlborough Downs, shaped, dressed to a curve of about 49 ft radius, and erected to form a circle. They were pointed at the bottom to fit into holes in the chalk and tenons were cut on their top surfaces, to receive mortices formed in 7 ton sarsen lintels, also dressed to 49 ft radius. The sarsen lintels were tongued and grooved to fit together endwise.

The layouts of many megalithic stone circles, including Stonehenge, have been accurately surveyed by Professor Alexander Thom, formerly Professor of Engineering at Oxford, and his son, Dr Archibald Thom. They have shown that the plans were based on carefully set out circles and ellipses.[1] Right-angled setting out lines had been laid down to arrive at axes and tangent points using Pythagorean triangles of various shapes (but not always exact, e.g. sides of 8, 9, 12 were used).[2]

It was well known that the orientation of certain stones at Stonehenge had astronomical connection with sunrise and sunset. The Thoms showed that this applied to many stone circles both for sun and moon observations. They also showed that the degree of accuracy was far higher than previously thought, because the two stones on the sight-line were orientated so that a feature on the horizon was the true foresight.

1. THOM A. and THOM A. S. *Megalithic remains in Britain and Brittany.* Clarendon Press, Oxford, 1978, Chapters 3 and 11.

2. WOOD J. E. *Sun, moon and standing stones.* Oxford University Press, Oxford, 1980, 39.

2. Queensberry Bridge, Amesbury and Ornamental Bridge, Amesbury

Queensberry Bridge, Amesbury:
HEW 1637
SU 151 413

Ornamental Bridge, Amesbury:
HEW 1638
SU 149 418

All John Smeaton's major bridges were built in the North of Great Britain. Of his three minor bridges in the South the two that remain are at Amesbury, Wilts., over the River Avon.[1–3]

The first, Queensberry Bridge, was built in 1775 to carry one of the London to Devon roads, later the A303. It is symmetrical with five segmental arches, the centre being 15 ft 6 in. span. The bridge is 105 ft long and 18 ft wide between parapets which are level. Amesbury now has an east–west bypass, so the bridge only carries local traffic.

In 1776 Smeaton prepared his only classical bridge design for a small structure in the Duke of Queensberry's private park. He called it the Ornamental Bridge. It is symmetrical, with three shallow elliptical arches, the centre span being 18 ft 6 in. The voussoirs have moulded top edges and the parapet is balustraded. The park is private.

Queensberry Bridge, Amesbury

1. Ruddock E. C. *Arch bridges and their builders 1735-1835*. Cambridge University Press, Cambridge, 1979, 90 and 95.

Ornamental Bridge, Amesbury

2. Skempton A. W. (ed.) *John Smeaton, FRS*. Thomas Telford, London, 1981, 172–173.

3. Designs of the late John Smeaton, FRS. Royal Society, 4, f 101–102 (Queensbury), f 95v–98 (Ornamental).

3. Salisbury Cathedral Tower

♣

HEW 508

SU 142 295

Salisbury Cathedral, built between 1220 and 1250, originally had a lantern over the crossing of the nave and transepts. The lantern was 115 ft above floor level. In 1330 work started on a 41 ft square tower, 109 ft high, surmounted by a 180 ft spire, making the total height 404 ft, the highest church building in Britain. Internal squinch arches were provided at the top of the tower to give continuous seating for the octagonal spire which is clad with 8 in. thick Portland stone.

The tower walls began to move outwards at the top, because of the estimated 300 tons horizontal thrust from the squinch arches, so the medieval builders inserted wrought iron ties adjacent to the arches. Sir Christopher Wren added diagonal ties across the tower in 1660 and more ties were added down the years. In 1938 an extra mullion was inserted behind each window and three of the four corner staircases in the tower were filled in with concrete. Consulting engineers, Gifford and Partners, have undertaken substantial remedial works including the provision of new stainless steel circumferential ties and a new reinforced concrete ring beam.

The crossing's four main columns are founded at a depth of only 4 ft with very little footing spread, so that their load, of 1750 tons each, results in a stress of about 15 tons/ft^2 on the gravel subsoil. Inevitably appreciable settlement occurred, fortunately uniformly, but since Sir Christopher Wren's report in 1660, settlement has been slight and in the past 20 years negligible.

4. Harnham Ancient Bridge, Salisbury and Fordingbridge Ancient Bridge

♣

Harnham Ancient Bridge: HEW 1489 SU 143 291

Fordingbridge Ancient Bridge: HEW 1550 SU 149 142

The River Avon is crossed by three large ancient bridges, Harnham, Fordingbridge, and Christchurch. (HEW 394). Harnham and Fordingbridge have two-centred pointed arches on ribs of two chamfered orders and are about the same age but the parapet of Fordingbridge is curved in elevation, which enhances its appearance.

Bishop Bingham built Harnham Bridge[1,2] in 1245 to improve access to Salisbury from the south. This became a factor in Salisbury's prosperity to the detriment of Wilton, 3 miles upstream. He chose the site of a ford and an island; thus there are two bridges. The smaller north bridge has three arches, one now filled in; the south bridge has six. All spans are 16 ft. Widening was carried out in 1774, the main bridge by 3 ft each side, the north birdge by a tapering amount, about 7 ft maximum on the west side only, using segmental arches.

Fordingbridge Bridge[3] was widened by 2 ft 3 in. each side in 1841, but the new arches springing from the cutwaters are slightly greater in span, so the original arches may still be seen. The bridge has seven arches and is 130 ft long. In 1901 it was widened again by a reinforced concrete cantilevered footpath on the upstream side.

There is a record of pontage for repair to the bridge in 1252.

Harnham Ancient Bridge

1. *Victoria County history of Wiltshire.* **6**, 88.

2. JERVOISE E. *The ancient bridges of the south of England.* Architectural Press, 1930, 72–74.

3. Ibid, 61, 75–76 and 80.

5. Christchurch Ancient Bridge ♣

HEW 394

SZ 161 927

This is a fine fifteenth or sixteenth century bridge over the River Avon near the centre of Christchurch.[1] Originally there were six segmental arches, average span 11 ft; subsequently the westernmost was filled in. Each arch has two orders, the inner voussoirs being grey limestone as the rest of the bridge, the outer voussoirs are red sandstone and set longitudinally.

In 1900 the bridge was widened by 10 ft on the up-

Christchurch
Ancient Bridge

stream side. Later a footpath was added, cantilevered on steelwork from the new masonry.

On the upstream west side there is, perhaps, the earliest example of the use of reinforced concrete sheet piling. A 100 ft length was driven in 1899, designed on the Mouchel-Hennebique system.[2] The piles are 2 ft wide, 8 in. thick, recessed on one edge and tongued on the other. They have cast-iron chisel edged shoes. A few were withdrawn in 1913 and found to be in good condition; the remainder are still *in situ*.

Until 1956 the bridge carried the A35 Southampton to Honiton road. A bypass to the town was then constructed, with a three-span prestressed concrete structure over the river. The older bridge still carries local traffic.

1. JERVOISE E. *The ancient bridges of the south of England.* Architectural Press, 1930, 75–76.

2. DE VESIAN J. S. E. and GUERITTE T. J. *Hennebique reinforced concrete: theory and practice.* L. G. Mouchel, London, 1921, 38.

6. Tuckton Bridge, Bournemouth ♣

This is an early example of a reinforced concrete multi-span road bridge, probably the first to carry a double track tramway. It was built over the River Stour in 1905 to replace a timber toll bridge on cast-iron piles.

HEW 993

SZ 149 923

The design is almost a direct substitution of reinforced concrete for timber members, except that the main spans have segmental arch ribs 12 in. deep, 11 in. wide, with a rise of 5 ft. The cross beams at the piers have a curved soffit, making them deeper at the ends, to provide lateral stability since the columns are unbraced lower down. The main arch ribs, with open spandrels above, support vertical columns, which, in turn, support the deck cross beams. At each pier there are three 14 in. square reinforced concrete piles continued up to deck level.

The footways are cantilevered 5 ft 6 in. on either side of the road, originally with clumsy reinforced concrete railings but these have been replaced by an elegant cast-iron design.

From abutment to abutment the bridge is 347 ft long, made up of a half span of 12 ft 9 in. at either end, eleven 25 ft 6 in. spans, and a centre span of 41 ft 2 in. for river traffic. The design was by Mouchel-Hennebique using their reinforcement system.

Tuckton Bridge, Bournemouth

For small multi-span road bridges a substantial design development was the introduction of heavy reinforced straight beams, which were easier to contruct than curved arch ribs and produced no end thrust which could be difficult to contain during construction. This development is illustrated by Bow Bridge, Kent (HEW 1392, Chapter p.234).

7. Meyrick Park Water Tower, Bournemouth

♣

HEW 174

SZ 084 916

The first reinforced concrete water tower in Britain, com-

Meyrick Park
Water Tower,
Bournemouth

pleted in 1900 was designed and built by Mouchel on the Hennebique system.[1]

It stands 50 ft high, with a 21 ft diameter, 10 ft deep, 15 000 gallon tank, supported on six 18 in. square columns. The circular tank, 5 in. thick, is monolithic with the supporting ring beam and is tied by 108 vertical $5/16$ in. diameter bars 12 ft 2 in. long, spaced around the circumference. The ring beam is finished as a moulded cornice and the columns have elaborate plinths and cappings, which resemble classical masonry facings.

Use for water supply was discontinued some years ago. For a time the structure was a meteorological station. The concrete is in fairly good condition, but appreciably discoloured.

1. COLLINS A. R. (ed.) *Structural engineering: two centuries of British achievement*. Tarot Print, Chislehurst 1983, 84.

8. Alum Chine Suspension Bridge, Bournemouth

♣

The coastline at Bournemouth is characterised by eight steeply sided valleys, or chines, in the Bracklesham beds, containing streams running down to the sea. Several of these valleys are public gardens and are bridged.

HEW 1255

SZ 071 905

Alum Chine is bridged twice for foot traffic, by a 67 ft span reinforced concrete arch, built in 1912, on the Mouchel-Hennebique system and a 230 ft span light steel suspension bridge designed and built by David Rowell and Company in 1904.

This latter bridge[1] consists of two three-hinged stiffened trusses, acting as parapets, suspended by mild steel hangers clamped to twin 6 by 19 steel catenary cables. These are suspended from tapered steel lattice pillars with finials, in pairs, and joined by simple portal bracing. The back stays to the towers are straight.

In 1973,[2] while the catenary cables were being renewed, the lattice towers were encased in concrete.

1. MARSHALL P. The repair and renovation of Alum Chine suspension bridge, Bournemouth. *J. Instn Mun. Engrs*, 1975, 102, 198–202.

2. ALLNUTT A. G. Association news and views, *New Civ. Engr*, 1973, 13 Dec., 51.

♣

HEW 918

SZ 009 908

Above: Town
Cellars, Poole

9. Town Cellars, Poole

Poole Harbour was a Roman port linked to Ackling Dyke (HEW 899). Later Wareham[1] was used, to be followed in medieval times by Poole again, as the channel to Wareham silted up. Although originating earlier, the stone building called Town Cellars[2] was rebuilt in the fifteenth century when Poole became a Port of the Staple. In 1512 it was called the Woolhouse.

Inside, the structure is 25 ft wide and was originally 120 ft long but in the nineteenth century, when Quay Street (now called Thames Street) was extended through it, the length was reduced to 70 ft. The floor has been excavated to its original level, 4 ft 6 in. below present quay level. The walls are 3 ft 6 in. thick at base, with external counterforts at truss positions. Windows and doors have pointed arches.

The roof covering is now of hand-made tiles but was probably originally stone slabs, as the oak roof trusses are massive. The latter have principal rafters with heavy eaves, tie beams and collars at mid-height, supporting two splayed struts to the principal rafters. Between the eaves tie and the collar there is a curved member on each side. These meet in the middle to form an arch. The building is now a nautical museum; the remaining west end is part of a public house.

Excavations[2] for drainage between Town Cellars and the quay have revealed an eighteenth century quay wall 12 ft high and 5 ft thick. It is probable that this conceals the remains of an older timber wharf.

1. MAY V. J. Reclamation and shoreline changes in Poole harbour. *Proc. Dorset Natural History and Archaeological Society*, 1968, 90 and 141–154.

2. HORSEY I. P. *Waterfront archaeology in north European towns. Poole, Dorset.* Borough of Poole Museum Service, 1979, 2–3.

10. White Mill Bridge, Sturminster Marshall

♣

HEW 376

ST 957 005

Jervoise[1] describes this bridge over the River Stour as the most beautiful in Dorset. It is also probably the oldest, having been built about 1175. Lying on the old Wimborne to Dorchester road it has been bypassed and, unlike many Dorset bridges, it has never been widened. Built in Norman style, each of its eight nearly semicircular arches of red sandstone has four chamfered ribs. The face rib stones are alternately white limestone and red sandstone.

Masonry parapets rest on distinctive straight lengths of string course supported by corbels. Coping stones are clamped together by iron dogs set in lead. Refuges are provided at each pier on both sides of the structure, which

White Mill Bridge, Sturminster Marshall

is 210 ft long and 12 ft wide. The largest arch span is 19 ft 6 in.

It is recorded that in 1341 three shillings were bequeathed for its repair.[2] Foundation underpinning was carried out to this Scheduled Ancient Monument in 1964.

1. JERVOISE E. *The ancient bridges of the south of England.* Architectural Press, 1930, 82.

2. WALLIS A. J. *Dorset bridges, a history and guide.* The Abbey Press, Sherborne, 1974, 61.

♠

HEW 849

ST968 034 to SU 022 178

11. Ackling Dyke

Ackling Dyke is the name given to the southern 16 miles of the Roman road from Old Sarum to a cross roads near the ancient earthworks called Badbury Rings, north-west of Wimborne, where it divides to go to Bath, Dorchester and Poole harbour.[1] This stretch is one of the finest lengths of Roman road in Britain, not only because of the beauty of the surrounding country but also because of the unusually generous proportions of the road between the Gussages (ST 99 11) and Woodyates (SU 03 19). For no apparent reason, the road embankment (agger) widens from the normal 21 ft to more than 40 ft and in places, it

Ackling Dyke

is raised 4 to 5 ft above ground level. Moreover the width between the flanking ditches widens to some 80 ft.

The course of the road is shown on Ordnance Survey sheets and is visible from the air. It runs nearly parallel to the Blandford Forum to Salisbury Road, A354, which it joins for a short distance before diverging north-east.

1. MARGARY J. D. *Roman roads in Britain*. John Baker, London, (3rd edn), 1973, 104–105.

12. Bagber Cast-iron Bridge ♣

HEW 893

ST 764 157

Bagber Bridge, which carries a minor road over the River Lydden near Sturminster Newton, has two interesting features. Wrought iron ties 1½ in. in diameter are used beneath the cast-iron girders to reduce tensile stress in the cast iron. This was also used for cast-iron beams in Portsmouth Dockyard, No 6 Boathouse, (HEW 739, p.157). Secondly the cast-iron girders have a segmental arch rib 6 in. deep, 2 ½ in. thick incorporated in their webs. The wrought iron ties are also evidently intended to counteract horizontal thrust from these arches. Thus the tensioning of the wrought iron ties was an early form of prestressing, as well as producing tied arches. There are

Bagber Cast-iron Bridge

four cast-iron H girders 31 ft in span, 2 ft deep, with 7 in. wide top (compression) flanges and 14 in. wide bottom (tension) flanges.

The names of the ingenious designer, W. Dawes, and the ironfounders, the Coalbrookdale Company, who cast the components for the world's first cast-iron bridge across the Severn Gorge at Coalbrookdale (HEW 136, SJ 672 034),[1] appear on plates fixed to the outside girders. The bridge dates from about 1850.

When it became necessary to strengthen the structure[2] it was given a lighter deck, and a load restriction was imposed, so that its appearance could be preserved.

1. SIVEWRIGHT W. J. *Civil engineering heritage: Wales and Western England.* Thomas Telford, London, 1986, 169–170.

2. WALLIS A. J. *Dorset bridges.* The Abbey Press, Sherborne, 1974, 52.

Below: Fifehead Neville Pack-horse Bridge

13. Fifehead Neville Packhorse Bridge

♣

HEW 896

ST 772 112

This is an attractive little two-span medieval bridge, which is sited next to a ford of the River Divelish. Each of the 6 ft spans is a pointed triangular arch with roughly shaped flat voussoirs.[1] Originally, to avoid obstruction to

loaded animals, there was only a 6 in. high parapet on either side. These have now been augmented by timber hand-railings. The centre pier has a cutwater only on the upstream side. The bridge is a Scheduled Ancient Monument.

1. Wallis A. J. *Dorset bridges*. The Abbey Press, Sherborne, 1974, 77–78.

14. Roman Aqueduct, Dorchester

The Romans constructed this aqueduct at the end of the first century to provide water for Durnovaria, now Dorchester. A supply was taken from the River Frome at Notton some 12 miles upstream at 275 ft above sea-level; this reached Dorchester at 250 ft, about 60 ft above the river. Thus the fall was only 25 ft in 12 miles, demonstrating Roman surveying skill.

For most of the way the aqueduct winds around the contours of the hills on the west side of the river valley. Places where it was notched into the slope are still visible. The bottom width of the channel was about 5 ft, with 1 in 2 side slopes and a depth of water of about 2 ft. Using a conservative roughness coefficient the delivery must have been some eight million gallons per day.

HEW 683

SY 614 956 to 688 906

Roman Aqueduct, Dorchester

The reservoir at Dorchester, fed by the aqueduct, has never been traced and there are no remains of intake works. The best place to view the aqueduct from the road is at Fordington Bottom (SY 672 916) on the old Roman road.

♣

15. Weymouth Port

HEW 1413

SY 680 787 to 688 789

Like Newhaven (HEW 1414, p.211), Weymouth is an ancient port in a tidal river mouth, now used primarily for ferry traffic. It dates from the fourteenth century, subsequently developing downstream through the town on the north bank of the River Wey. As ships became larger the depth alongside the masonry quay walls was

increased by providing timber and later reinforced concrete piled aprons.

In 1794 Weymouth became the official Post Office mail port for the Channel Islands. In 1857 the Great Western Railway arrived and in 1865 mixed gauge track was laid through the streets to the quayside. Extensive reclamation, retained by steel sheet piling, was completed in 1971 to provide roll-on, roll-off facilities and the necessary vehicle parking areas.

The entrance width is 420 ft, dredged to 17 ft below low water of spring tides. In 1903 the west breakwater was extended to minimize disturbance in the entrance caused by waves reflected off the northernmost Portland Harbour breakwater (HEW 124) which had been completed a few years earlier.

16. Portland Harbour

Portland Harbour, the largest artificial harbour in the United Kingdom, has the unusual advantage that it is protected from the worst gales, south-west to west, by its landward side, comprising the Isle of Portland and Chesil Bank. The harbour area was only fully exposed to the east.

HEW 124

SY 700 760

Construction of the two southern breakwaters[1] started in 1849 to the design of James Rendel, after the foundation stone was laid by the Prince Consort. With abundant stone available on Portland, Rendel inevitably chose a tipped mound design — called pierre perdue. Unlike in Plymouth Breakwater (HEW 126, p.47) small stones were not rejected and the method was described as 'tipping promiscuously'. This form of construction was also used at Alderney and at Holyhead (HEW 1095, SH 25 84).[2]

Loaded wagons were run out over tracks laid on temporary timber trestles for tipping. The largest stones weighed 7 tons. At the greatest depth, 50 ft below low water,[3] the base width of the mound was 255 ft, the lower slopes were 1 in 1½. At a depth of 12 ft below low water the seaward slope eased to 1 in 6, to minimize draw down in the wave disturbance zone. After Rendel died in 1856 his Resident Engineer, John Coode, completed construction by 1868. The Contractor was J. T. Leather of Leeds.

Opposite:
Weymouth Port

135

Portland Harbour   The two northern breakwaters put in hand in 1893 as
protection against torpedo attack, completed the enclosure of 2 sq. miles of water by 15 000 ft of breakwater with
three entrances.

For defence use the two southern breakwaters were
given paved roadways protected by 20 ft high parapet
walls. All entrances had vertical ashlar masonry walls,

which were granite faced above low water and semicircular in plan.

In 1914 the south entrance was blocked by sinking the battleship *HMS Hood* across it on the outside. This was a defence measure but it also reduced wave action at some berths during south-east gales.

1. SCOTT M. Description of a breakwater at the port of Blyth; and of improvements in breakwaters, applicable to harbours of refuge. *Min. Proc. Instn Civ. Engrs*, 1858–59, **18**, 79.

2. SIVEWRIGHT W. J. *Civil engineering heritage: Wales and Western England.* Thomas Telford, London, 1986, 7–9.

3. MILLER D. Structures in the sea, without cofferdams; with a description of the works of the new Albert Harbour at Greenock. *Min. Proc. Instn Civ. Engrs*, 1862–63, **22**, 431 and Plate 9A.

17. Lyme Regis Harbour

The small harbour at Lyme Regis called the Cobb, dating from about 1300, is one of the earliest artificial harbours in Britain. The site and layout was evidently chosen to make use of the limestone outcrops in the seabed, but they alternate with layers of clay, which has led to difficulties.

In 1805 the Board of Ordnance, who were responsible for maintenance, sought the advice of William Jessop, then one of the most eminent engineers in the country. His report began by stating that geological conditions had caused the cliff face to recede 270 ft since the harbour

HEW 414

SY 339 915

Lyme Regis Harbour

was built. All the original work was in local lias limestone but the army engineers had brought in Portland stone which he approved. Major repairs took place in 1825.

The main curving south-west arm, 900 ft long and about 40 ft wide, with a parapet almost half full width and about 12 ft high, acts as a breakwater against prevailing south-west storms and also provides the berths. Store buildings for fishing gear are sited adjacent to the berths on the breakwater.

The eastern breakwater, 19 ft high and 12 ft wide with a low parapet, is now detached from the shore because of land recession, but the gap has been closed by pell mell block work, an easy task because the harbour now dries at low water as a result of local accretion. Local fishing boats operate but the harbour's main use now is for recreation.

Charmouth Road
Tunnel

18. Charmouth Road Tunnel and Beaminster Road Tunnel

Road tunnels are rare in the South of England, but two were driven through steep greensand scarps in Dorset. The first was at Thistle Hill, Charmouth on the A35 Southampton to Honiton road. It is 220 ft long and was completed in 1831. It substantially reduced the ruling gradient from 1 in 5 to a short stretch at 1 in 8, to 1 in 12 at the Charmouth end. It also cut 50 ft off the climb.

Charmouth Road Tunnel: HEW 980 SY 349 948

Beaminster Road Tunnel: HEW 899 ST 468 032

The second, Horn Hill tunnel, is on the A3066 Beaminster to Crewkerne road.[1] It reduced the gradient from 1 in 6 to 1 in 10, the length of the road by a mile, and avoided a climb of 50 ft. The length is 345 ft, walls are brickwork[2] 3 ft 6 in. thick, and the arch, also brick, is 2 ft 9 in. thick. Completion was in 1832. Both portals are listed as of Special Architectural or Historic Interest.

The Engineer was Michael Lane, a pupil of Sir Marc Brunel.

1. *British bridges*. Public Works, Roads and Transport Congress. London, 1933, 79.

2. WALLIS A. J. *Dorset bridges*. The Abbey Press, Sherborne, 1974, 85.

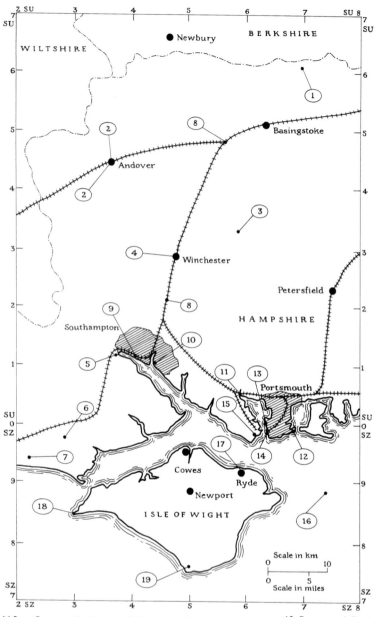

1. Stratfield Saye Cast-iron Bridge
2. Upper Clatford and Ladies Walk Bridges
3. Alresford Ancient Dam
4. Winchester Cathedral underpinning
5. Eling Tide Mill
6. Mass Concrete Tower, Sway
7. Chewton Glen Bridge
8. London to Southampton Railway
9. Southampton Docks
10. Woolston Reinforced Concrete Jetty
11. Fareham Viaducts
12. Portsmouth Main Drainage
13. Portsmouth Dockyard
14. *Mary Rose*
15. Ship testing tank, Haslar
16. Nab Tower
17. Ryde Pier
18. The Needles Lighthouse
19. St Catherine's Lighthouse

6. Hampshire and Isle of Wight

South Hampshire is dominated by the cities of Portsmouth and Southampton. Both have developed as ports of international renown, the former as a Royal Naval base located at the south of the tidal inlet which forms Portsmouth Harbour. The latter, in the shelter of Southampton Water, was a commercial port, which for many decades was the nation's principal terminus for ocean going liners. Especially during the nineteenth century, the economic fortunes of Southampton thrived in times of peace, whereas Portsmouth prospered in times of war. Both have outstanding examples of maritime works. Southampton's King George V Graving Dock was the last of a series of dry docks which were the world's largest in their time and were constructed to keep pace with the rapid increase in passenger ship size. A number of Portsmouth Dockyard's facilities are amongst the oldest still in use. Both Nelson's flagship, *Victory*, and Henry VIII's, *Mary Rose*, are located in older dry docks within the traditional area of the Dockyard. The raising of the latter from the seabed of the Solent was in itself an engineering achievement of substance. Other maritime works include The Needles and St Catherine's Lighthouses on the Isle of Wight and the Nab Tower which carries an offshore light in the approaches to Spithead. The latter, completed in the early 1920s, illustrates some of the concepts and techniques used 40 years later to construct off-shore facilities to exploit North Sea oil reserves. The Haslar Model Testing Tank marks a very important stage in the development of using scale models to design and test ships. Modelling techniques, pioneered by Froude at Haslar, are now used in a wide range of civil and other engineering design applications. Across the Solent at Ryde, the nation's first major seaside pier was built in 1814 and until 1927 carried part of the track of Britain's first standard gauge electric railway. Another 'first' is located within Southampton Water where a jetty at Woolston was innovatively constructed in reinforced concrete.

The region's transport systems have tended either to connect the major urban conurbations along the coast, as does the relatively short and isolated M27 motorway, or to connect the major Solent ports to the capital, as illustrated by the London and Southampton Railway, which was very closely associated with the development and success of Southampton Docks. The area's topography, in conjunction with the design approach of Joseph Locke, who was responsible for many of the area's railways, has resulted in few railway structures of note. Some of the best examples, the Viaducts at Fareham, are only around 30 ft high.

Unlike other regions, there are few ancient masonry bridges of note, but the bridges at Stratfield Saye, Upper Clatford and Andover (Ladies Walk) are good examples of nineteenth century ironwork. Although the rib arches are not readily visible on Chewton Glen Bridge, their reinforced concrete construction was a pioneering use of the material.

The area contains a number of other works which illustrate the range of activities undertaken by civil engineers. There is a dam at Alresford built around 1200, difficult underpinning has been undertaken at Winchester Cathedral and a tide mill and associated works have existed at Eling for many centuries. Although the design origin and motivation for the Sway Tower is marked by some fanciful stories, as a structure it represents a pioneering use of mass concrete in tall buildings.

Stratfield Saye
Cast-iron Arch
Bridge

1. Stratfield Saye Cast-iron Arch Bridge

♦

HEW 1344

SU 696 612

This is an elegant cast-iron arch bridge in a private estate which was given to the Duke of Wellington by the nation after the battle of Waterloo. It takes one of the carriage drives over the River Loddon. Built to the design of Thomas Wilson in 1802, it was one of the smaller bridges he designed between 1800 and 1810; a larger one, Tickford Bridge, Newport Pagnell (HEW 52, SP 877 438), is also still in use.[1,2]

The open web segmental 8 ft rise arch ribs have spandrels of diminishing circles giving a light graceful appearance. There are four main arch ribs, each of five segments, and at each joint there is inserted a rectangular cast-iron frame the full width of the bridge, to give lateral stability. This arrangement was patented by Wilson in 1802. Ironwork was cast by Walkers of Rotherham. The arch span is 40 ft, the width between parapets is 13 ft 6 in. and the decking is timber planking. The abutments are of masonry and somewhat heavy looking. They increase the overall length of the bridge to 70 ft.

1. JAMES J. G. The cast-iron bridges of Thomas Wilson. *Trans. Newcomen Soc.*, 1978, 50, 60.

2. RUDDOCK E. C. *Arch bridges and their builders 1735–1835*. Cambridge University Press, 1979, 159–160.

2. Upper Clatford Bridge and Ladies Walk Bridge, Andover

Upper Clatford Bridge:
HEW 502
SU 357 435

Ladies Walk Bridge, Andover:
HEW 653
SU 375 452

These two attractive little cast-iron bridges came from the foundry of Tasker and Fowle at Andover. Two more bridges were cast, but they have not survived.

Upper Clatford, 1843, is a two-span bridge over the River Anton. Most unusually all components are of cast-iron, including the river pier, wing wall and abutments and all components slot together without bolts. Only ten patterns were required. The greatest number of casts from one mould were the twelve inner girders. Taskers may have intended to mass produce this design but it was not repeated.

The bridge is 12 ft wide, with two 13 ft spans; the outer

Ladies Walk
Bridge

main beams were cast as open spandrel segmental shallow arch ribs with diminishing circles in the spandrels and an edge curb. Perhaps uniquely, the river pier is a cast-iron plate, ⅝ in. thick on edge but stiffened at 2 ft centres with 2 in. ribs. All panels have a rose at their centres.

When the bridge was Listed Grade II the County Surveyor made a fine job of restoration, providing hidden deck strengthening and replacing damaged parapet railings to the original cast and wrought iron design.

In Andover Museum there is a model bridge made by Taskers. It resembles Upper Clatford, but is not so attractive. It may have been intended to help sell mass produced bridges.

Ladies Walk, 1851, is an elegant little footbridge sited just east of the town, where the now disused London Road is in a cutting. There are three segmental cast-iron ribs 40 ft 6 in. long, jointed at the centre. The rise is 3 ft, spandrel infill being diminishing circles cast with the rib. Plain vertical hand railing is stabilised by attractive curved cast-iron bracket members at 6 ft centres. The width is 5 ft 3 in.

3. Alresford Ancient Dam

Alresford Dam,[1,2] originally called the Great Ware, was built by Bishop Godfrey de Lucy in 1200 to impound water for a 200 acre fish pond on the River Alre, a tributary of the River Itchen. The crest of the dam became used as a causeway, avoiding marshy ground on the London to Southampton road. This continued until a turnpike road was constructed on the line of the A31 in about 1753.

HEW 541

SU 588 330

The dam, mainly of chalk fill, is 2000 yd long, 20 ft high and 30 ft wide at the crest. The downstream side slope is very steep, at about 1 in 1½, and tree covered. Due to siltation, the area of water is now only some 30 acres.

Water level was controlled by sluices known as the Shettles at the south end of the dam, the discharge passing through the dam in a masonry lined channel under a stone arch bridge carrying the road on the crest, now the B3046, Alresford to Basingstoke road. A series of weirs in the channel now control the discharge.

Probably the 25 ft high Oldstead Grange Dam, near Byland Abbey, North Yorkshire, is the only dam built at that time which was larger than Alresford.

1. ROBERTS E. *Proc. Hants Field Club and Archaeological Soc.*, 1985, **41**, 127–138.

2. SMITH N. *A history of dams.* Davies, London, 1971, 164–5.

4. Winchester Cathedral underpinning

Winchester Cathedral, at 556 ft, claims to be the longest in Britain. The height to the roof ridge is 77 ft. It was built in three main periods:

HEW 182

SU 482 292

1. *1079–93.* Walkelyn's original Norman church
2. *1200* A rectangular retro-choir at the east end in the early English style in place of the Norman apse, by Bishop Godfrey de Lucy
3. *1360–1404* Transformation of the nave from Norman to Perpendicular by Bishop Edington and William of Wykeham.

Since the beginning of the twentieth century, great efforts have been made to preserve the stability of the structure. In 1906 the east end of the cathedral began to show serious subsidence, with cracks appearing and walls and columns tilting up to 10° out of plumb. The zone worst affected was around Bishop de Lucy's retro-choir and Lady Chapel.

Francis Fox was appointed as Consulting Engineer. Immediate measures comprised shoring walls and erecting centring in arches. Pressure grouting cracked walls was also started — an early example of this treatment. The cracking largely arose from the Norman practice of using dry rubble as wall and column coring. Some 16½ tons of steel was also used for tie rods inserted at various strategic positions.

The cause of the trouble lay in the wall foundations which were timber rafts resting on beds of marl and peat, the latter having shrunk due to lowering of the ground water table. Shafts were opened along the outside of the affected walls and the rafts, timber and peat excavated to water level. Thereafter a diver was employed to complete the dig down to hard gravel and to build a new foundation of concrete bagwork, mass concrete and brick footings to the underside of the old masonry.

The Contractors were John Thompson of Peterborough but all the underwater work was done by one man, William Robert Walker, chief diver with Siebe Gorman and Company, makers of diving equipment. In his six years at Winchester, he laid some 26 000 bags of concrete, 150 000 concrete blocks and 100 000 engineering bricks. This feat caught the imagination of the public and was recognised by the award of the Royal Victorian Order by King George V and later by the small commemorative statue which stands today near the Lady Chapel. Francis Fox was knighted in 1912.

Subsequent strengthening of the cathedral fabric has included the addition of ten flying buttresses along the south transept in 1912 and pressure grouting some of the main columns in the nave in the 1960s.[1,2]

1. GREEN G. E. Groundwater problems encountered during hotel construction at Winchester. *Proc. Instn Civ. Engrs*, 1964, 28, 171–186.

2. Ibid. (Discussion). *Proc. Instn Civ. Engrs*, 1964, 29, 819–822.

5. Eling Tide Mill and Causeway ♣

HEW 1400

SU 365 125

There has been a mill at Eling since the Domesday Survey of 1086, but the earliest mention of the causeway in surviving documents is 1418, when it was in need of repair. It is probable that the tide mill dates to at least that time.

The causeway is about 250 ft long, 54 ft wide and carries a 16 ft metalled road on its crest, 9 ft above low water. Most of what is visible is modern, including much bag work, but on the down-stream face under the mill, which is built on the causeway, the roughly coursed stonework appears older.[1] Water is trapped by the causeway in a tidal inlet where the Bartley Water joins Southampton Water, so that at low tide the head can be used to drive the two water-wheels in the mill. Each tide provides four hours running time starting with a head of 6 ft.

The tide mill is now leased from the New Forest District Council by a Trust, who have restored it, opened it to the public and grind stone-ground flour for sale.

1. WAILES R. Tide mills in England and Wales. *Trans. Newcomen Soc.,* 1938–39, 19, 1–33.

Eling Tide Mill

6. Sway Tower, Sway

HEW 173

SZ 280 967

This remarkable tower, 215 ft high and 18 ft square, may well be the first tall mass concrete structure in the United Kingdom.[1] It was built by a retired Indian Legal Service Judge A. A. T. Petersen. Apparently he was persuaded to build it after a seance when the medium, one of the workmen on his estate, allegedly contacted Sir Christopher Wren. Details of dimensions, construction methods, etc., were to be provided by Wren at subsequent seances.[2]

Sway Tower,
Sway

Petersen already had experience of mass concrete construction as he had taken down all the buildings on his estate and replaced them in the same material. He worried about having to discharge men when there was much unemployment in the neighbourhood and was thus receptive to this outlandish idea.

A 9 ft external octagonal staircase leads to 13 floors, supported on cast-iron beams. The tower is 2 ft thick at the bottom and 1 ft thick at the top. Construction proceeded in 1 ft 6 in. lifts using an internal working platform. The construction joints look like courses.

In December 1879, while the tower was being built, the Tay Bridge disaster occurred and the high wind pressures quoted in articles and letters to the press (up to 55 lb/ft^2) caused Petersen to call in Rollo Massey, a Consulting Engineer, to check the stability of his tower. Massey was satisfied both with the work and the ultimate stability of the complete tower.

The tower still stands and the concrete appears only to suffer from minor blemishes and shrinkage cracks.

1. *Occasional magazine of Milford on Sea Record Society.* 1927, **4**, June, 1.

2. REINA P. The supernaturalists' monument to cement. *New Civ. Engnr*, 1974, 16 May, 32.

7. Chewton Glen Bridge

Chewton Glen, Barton-on-Sea, is claimed, to be the first reinforced concrete arch bridge in the United Kingdom. This pioneering material use was the result of a mistake in the original design. The bridge, which now carries the A337, Lymington to Christchurch road, over the Walkford Brook, was built in 1900 as a 36° skew brick arch structure of 18 ft square span and 22 ft 3 in. skew span.[1]

Brick arch courses were laid parallel to the abutments instead of square to the road centre line. Evidently the County Surveyor was worried about the oblique thrust at the faces of the arch and agreement was reached, with the contractor, on a remedial scheme which involved strengthening with reinforced concrete arches 6ft wide on each side of the bridge, to be cast on top of the brick arch. The detailed design was by L. G. Mouchel using Hennebique reinforced concrete. Each reinforced concrete

HEW 172

SZ 224 938

Chewton Glen
Bridge

arch consists of two 12 in. by 8 in. ribs at 5 ft 4 in. centres, joined by a 5 in. slab making the total rib depth 17 in. At the abutment there are splay pieces from the inside acute angle ribs to distribute the thrust over a greater width of abutment. The design load was a 20 ton steam traction engine with 7½ tons on each driving wheel.

The parapets and spandrels are of brickwork which disguises the existence of the reinforced concrete ribs.

1. BOSTICO M. Early concrete bridges in Britain. *Concrete*, 1970, 4 Sep., 363–366.

8. The London to Southampton Railway

In 1826, a group of Southampton business men proposed a London to Southampton railway,[1,2] to develop the port and its trade. They intended that trains should run to Basingstoke and then to Bristol as well as southwards to Southampton.

In 1831 the London and Southampton Railway Company was formed and Frances Giles was appointed Engineer. He proposed a route with easy curves and gradients. He sited his London terminus at Nine Elms (TQ296 773).

The scheme was authorised in 1834, but without the lines westward from Basingstoke, prevented by the development of Brunel's Great Western Railway.[3]

Work started immediately, but by 1837 progress was so far behind schedule that the Directors replaced Giles by Joseph Locke, who had just completed the Grand Junction Railway between Birmingham and Newton le Willows (HEW 1129, SP 078371 to SJ 578951).[4]

Locke replaced a number of small contractors by Thomas Brassey on sections requiring major earthworks. He also made alterations in alignment to reduce cutting depths through St George's Hill, Weymouth and to reduce tunnelling in the high chalk at Popham.

Major engineering structures were avoided, but an attractive aqueduct was provided at Frimley to carry the Basingstoke Canal (HEW 1575, TQ 055 620 to SU 640 523) over the railway.

Locke used 15 ft long flat-bottom wrought iron rails laid on cast-iron chairs spiked to timber and sleepers. This gave a smoother ride than stone sleepers and cost less than Brunel's continuous longitudinal timber beams.

In 1839 a branch from Eastleigh (SU4519) to Gosport was authorised, and at the same time the company's name was changed to London and South Western.

The line between London and Southampton was completed in 1840 and the branch to Gosport in 1841.

At the London end the line was extended to Waterloo in 1848.

HEW 1481

TQ 310 799 to
SU 427 111

1. MARSHALL G. F. D. *A history of the Southern Railway*. Southern Railway, London, 1936, 69–88.

2. WILLIAMS R. A. *The London and South Western Railway. Vol. 1*. David and Charles, Newton Abbot, 1968, 11–47.

3. SIVEWRIGHT W. J. *Civil engineering heritage: Wales and Western England*. Thomas Telford, London, 1986, 97–100.

4. Ibid. 153-155 and 196-197.

5. SIVEWRIGHT W. J. op cit., 153–155 and 196–197.

9. Southampton Docks: Trafalgar Dry Dock, King George V Dry Dock, Ocean Dock and River Test Quay

Trafalgar Dry Dock:
HEW 891
SU 423 106

King George V Dry Dock:
HEW 1586
SU 394 123

Ocean Dock:
HEW 1614
SU 424 104

River Test Quay:
HEW 1587
SU 395 123 to 415 112

Southampton is sited at the confluence of the River Itchen with the estuary of the River Test. It is very sheltered and benefits from a double crested tidal cycle. A port, Clausentum, was originally established in Roman times. Until 1842, dock facilities were confined within the limits of the medieval town walls.[1] In 1836, the Southampton Dock Company was formed which developed the port in close association with the London and South Western Railway Company (HEW 1481). Their initial development, the Outer Dock, completed in 1842, was one of the first to include rail access to quays for passenger trains.

As ocean going liners increased in size, it proved necessary to provide even larger quays and dry docks to establish, and then retain, Southampton's position as the nation's premier liner port. This resulted in Southampton successively claiming the world's largest dry dock. No. 3 dry dock was built by Alfred Giles in 1846 and lengthened in 1854. The Prince of Wales dry dock, No. 5, was completed in 1895, three years after the London and South Western Railway had acquired the dock system. However, only a few years later it was necessary to provide an even larger facility, the Trafalgar dry dock. It was 860 ft long, 9 ft wide at the entrance, 43 ft deep and was opened in 1905 on the centenary of Nelson's famous victory. The original steel mitre gates were replaced by a sliding caisson in 1912 when the dock was lengthened by 22 ft and widened to accommodate the *Olympic*, *Titanic* and also the *Aquitania* then under construction. A further modification to the dock head was undertaken in 1922 for

Trafalgar Dock

the *Berengaria*. About the same time, a 60 000 ton floating dock was provided for the *Majestic* and *Leviathan*, after which development was planned on a grand scale. The King George V dry dock was opened by the King in 1933 to accommodate ships up to 100 000 tons. It was 1200 ft long and 135 ft wide and was constructed within a cofferdam. Nevertheless, it was necessary to sink ten deep pump wells to relieve upward pressure during construction of the unvented 25 ft thick mass concrete floor. F. E. Wentworth-Shields, Chief Docks Engineer, directed the work, which was able to accommodate Cunard's famous *Queen Mary* and *Queen Elizabeth*.

Other significant facilities include the Ocean Dock,[2] completed in 1911 and the River Test Quay,[3] associated with 407 acres of reclamation, which was completed in 1936. The former is a distinctive parallelogram-shaped tidal basin providing two main 1600 ft long quays, giving a total of five 800 ft berths. The quay wall is of mass concrete, 39 ft at the base, 10 ft at the top and 75 ft high. The basin, approach channel and turning area were dredged to give a 40 ft depth below low water of spring tides. The River Test Quay is 7542 ft long and was constructed by sinking a line of 146 concrete monoliths, 45 ft square in plan. It did not prove possible to achieve the required sinking depth and, to ensure stability, a wedge of earth was removed from the rear. This necessitated a bridging of 4 ft 6 in. thick reinforced concrete slabs spanning from the monoliths to a series of reinforced concrete piles. Part of the quay length was dredged to 40 ft and part to 45 ft below low water of spring tides.

1. BIRD J. *The major seaports of the United Kingdom.* Hutchinson, London, 1963, 154–180.

2. WENTWORTH-SHIELDS F. E. The construction of the 'White Star' dock and adjoining quays at Southampton. *Min. Proc. Instn Civ. Engrs,* 1913–14, Part 1, **195**, 42–147.

3. McHAFFIE M. G. J. Southampton docks extension. *J. Instn Civ. Engrs,* 1937–8, **9**, 184–236.

10. Woolston Reinforced Concrete Jetty

◆

HEW 98

SU 435 110

This was the first reinforced concrete jetty built in the United Kingdom. It was designed in 1898 by L. G. Mouchel for the London and South Western Railway using Hennebique's reinforcement system. The jetty head is 100 ft long and 46 ft wide, supported on 10 in. square reinforced concrete piles at 10 ft centres each way.

The design load was 2.3 tons/yd^2, the deck being 7 in. thick with primary and secondary beams at 10 ft centres. When built, the berth, which is on the east bank of the River Itchen, dried at low water and had 4 ft alongside at high water neap tide. Later it was incorporated into an extensive jetty complex and became part of a shipyard working for the Ministry of Defence, so that public access was denied.

The design followed timber jetty traditions, the piling being braced horizontally and diagonally in the tidal zone. It was not until the 1920s that raking piles began to be used to eliminate bracing and thick deck slabs eliminated the necessity for elaborate deck beam formwork at the same time providing a high degree of fixity for pile heads.

11. Fareham Viaducts

♣

HEW 1415

SU 579 060 to
581 060

SU 585 062 to
588 064

Hampshire has few railway viaducts, mainly because of low relief. However, there are two long viaducts, opened in 1848 and designed by Joseph Locke, on the Fareham to Portsmouth line, along the edge of a tidal creek.

The more westerly, Quay Street Viaduct, over the A32 Alton to Gosport road has ten 30 ft span segmental arches and one 34° skew arch of 36 ft span. The adjacent Porchester Road Viaduct has 16, 30 ft-span, semicurcular arches and also one 36 ft span, 34° skew arch. Both skew arches are dog-toothed. Red brick with stone cappings and brick string courses were used in both structures. The viaducts are only about 30 ft from ground to rail level and they cut off views of the attractive creek. Both are Listed Grade II.

The only other large viaduct in use in this area is Hurstbourne, (HEW 506, SU 430 489) on the Basingstoke to Salisbury line, built in 1854. It is unusual because the high tapering piers have elegant curved edges both in side and end elevation.

Fareham Viaduct

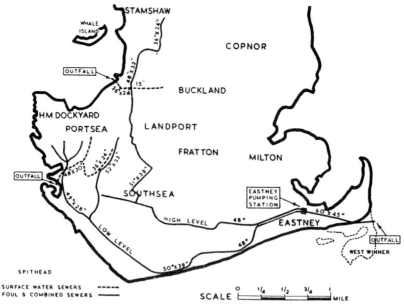

STAMSHAW

WHALE ISLAND

COPNOR

OUTFALL

15"

BUCKLAND

H.M.DOCKYARD
PORTSEA

LANDPORT

FRATTON

MILTON

OUTFALL

SOUTHSEA

EASTNEY PUMPING STATION

HIGH LEVEL   48"

EASTNEY

LOW LEVEL

48"

OUTFALL

WEST WINNER

SPITHEAD

SURFACE WATER SEWERS -----
FOUL & COMBINED SEWERS ——

SCALE

0 1/4 1/2 3/4 1
MILE

12. Portsmouth Main Drainage

♦

HEW 504

SU 674 992

Above:
Portsmouth Main
Drainage, 1870.
Courtesy of
Portsmouth City
Records Office

The City of Portsmouth is on a flat island of 9 sq. miles, separating Portsmouth Harbour from Langstone Harbour.

By 1868 a main drainage system had been installed with 11 miles of 4 ft diameter sewers having a fall of 1 in 5000.[1] The untreated sewage was pumped to sea on the ebb tide at the entrance to Langstone Harbour. As the population increased, difficulties occurred. The discharge was intermittent, as it could only take place on the ebb, so sewage accumulated in the sewers. Attempts to overcome this difficulty by pumping for longer periods made little improvement in the sewers and resulted in beach fouling.

In 1882, when the population was 150 000, Sir Frederick Bramwell was consulted. He recommended three retaining tanks of 4 500 000 gallons total capacity, into which the sewage could be pumped continuously and two 150 h.p. steam pumps capable of emptying the retaining tanks into the sea through three 42 in. diameter cast-iron pipes in the two hours of maximum ebb.

The works were put in hand and completed in 1887. Construction was by J. Mowlem and Company and en-

gine fabrication by James Watt and Company. The 72 ft
high Eastney pumphouse (HEW 504, SZ 672 993) and
chimney are a fine example of Victorian industrial architecture using polychrome brickwork.

Below:
Portsmouth No.
5 Dock.
Courtesy of the
Department of
the Environment.

Crown ©

Submersible electric pumps have superseded the compound beam engines, which have been restored for public demonstration; the pumphouse is now one of the city
museums. Unfortunately the chimney was reduced to
half its original height.

1. DANIEL H. F. *A history of Portsmouth drainage 1865–1956*. City of
Portsmouth Corporation, 1956.

◆

13. HM Dockyard, Portsmouth: No. 1 Basin and Dock Group, No. 5 Dock and No. 6 Boathouse

No I Basin and
Dock Group:
HEW 890
SU 627 007

The oldest part of Portsmouth Dockyard is the south-
west sector adjacent to the main gate on The Hard. It
centres on No. 1 (non tidal) Basin with Nos 5, 4, 3 and 2
Docks. Activities started in 1212, with major development in 1496 and 1658, but, being timber, the quays and
docks have been replaced by No. 1 Basin and No. 5 Dock,

No 5 DOCK:
HEW 123
SU 628 007

No 6
Boathouse:
HEW 739
SU 630 004

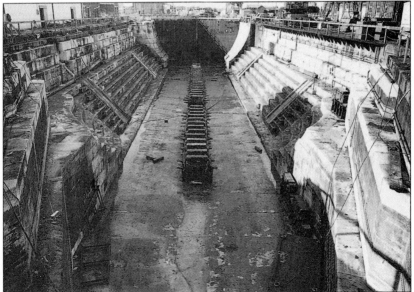

No. 6 Boathouse, Portsmouth Dock. Courtesy of the Department of the Environment. Crown ©

the first masonry structures. These, together with No. 1 Dock Devonport (HEW 1117, p.44), were built by Templar and Parlby, between 1692 and 1698 to the design of Edmund Dummer, Surveyor to the Navy Board. Purbeck stone faced with Portland was used and all dock and quay walls and timber dock floors were founded on a grillage of timber piles. The entrance widths were 55 ft with mitre gates, the water depth was 17 ft and dock length was 210 ft.

In 1764 the basin width was increased by moving No. 5 Dock 40 ft east on its axis, involving a new head and entrance. The basin entrance was modified and deepened by 2 ft. In 1772 No. 4 Dock was built, replacing a slipway, and in 1777 a reservoir was formed to the north for draining down Nos 5 and 4 Docks; this had previously been done by continuous chain bucket pumps operated by capstans worked by six horses.

In 1796 the new Director General of Naval Works, Brigadier Sir Samuel Bentham, brother of philosopher Jeremy Bentham, started to enlarge No. 1 Basin southwards with a new entrance and two docks, Nos 3 and 2. The contract again went to Templar and Parlby. The new entrance had an inverted elliptical arch floor, a design used at Ringsend docks, Dublin, in 1791 by William Jessop.[1] Bentham's gate was a floating caisson type, a continental idea. This allowed a roadway across the entrance, not feasible with mitre gates. No. 3 Dock, the last in the group, was given an inverted masonry arch floor. The timber floors of the other docks have subsequently been replaced.

The Navy's need for pulley blocks was enormous, so Bentham persuaded the Navy Board to install mass production block making machinery, designed by Sir Marc Brunel, in a building erected over the reservoir referred to above. The machinery was made by Henry Maudslay and started production in 1808.

No. 6 Boathouse, Portsmouth Dock. Courtesy of the Department of the Environment. Crown ©

Since 1922, No. 2 Dock has housed HMS *Victory*. She is set up so that the dock coping is level with her water line. A permanent concrete cofferdam replaced the old gates. *Mary Rose* lies in No. 3 Dock. Both ships are open to the public and were joined in 1987 by *Warrior*, moored alongside a new jetty, with access just inside the dockyard main gate.

Close to the dock is No. 6 Boathouse, which is a fine yellow brick industrial building with stone dressings. It is 164 ft long, 120 ft wide, with floor to floor heights of 19 ft 4 in., 16 ft, and 10 ft 3 in. to roof truss ties. Engineering interest centres in the grid of columns and beams to enable the upper floors to be strong enough to accept boats.

Cast-iron Tuscan columns of 1 ft 6 in. diameter at base, set on a 40 ft by 10 ft grid, support cast-iron I beams with a clear span of 38 ft 9 in. The beams are 2 ft 9 in. deep with 13 in. wide bottom flanges, 5 in. top flanges and 2 in. thick webs. Cast in the web are the words 'Load on this girder should not exceed 40 tons'. This corresponds to a floor loading of about 200 lb/ft^2. The beams have a wrought iron tie system consisting of two 4½ in. by 2 in. wrought iron flats under the bottom flange, tensioned by taper keys to relieve the beam of tension. Elaborate pinned supporting points are provided at the ⅓ span positions to minimise friction during tensioning. The secondary beams are also cast-iron, 10 ft 9 in. span, with arched supports.

The drawings of the main beam were signed by Lt R. N. Beatson, RE and dated 1845. The system of tensioning was also used on Bagber Bridge (HEW 893, p.131).

1. HADFIELD C. and SKEMPTON A. W. *William Jessop, engineer*. David and Charles, Newton Abbot, 1979, 259.

♠

HEW 1569

SU 628 007

14. Recovery of *Mary Rose*

The Tudor warship *Mary Rose* was commissioned in 1512 and given a major refit in 1536. At the same time a novel armament system, using cannon firing through ports in the hull, was introduced. Her main armament was 91 heavy guns.

In 1545, she capsized and sank off Southsea while

sailing to engage a French squadron off the Isle of Wight. Her hulk settled in the Solent silt which preserved all timbers more than 3 ft below seabed level, including most of her starboard side and the keel area, because she lay at 60° to the vertical.

About 400 years later she was located. Then, in 1979 the Mary Rose Trust was set up to recover artefacts from the ship for study and display and, if possible, to salvage the hull. R. J. Crocker and Partners were retained to devise a lifting system in collaboration with Lt Cdr J. Evans, a salvage consultant, and then to design the special structures required.

A floating crane was used to lower a flat 115 ft by 50 ft tubular steel lifting frame on adjustable corner legs astride the hull. This was attached to the frame by one hundred ½ in. diameter wire ropes fixed to bolts through the hull. These had been inserted by Royal Engineer divers who had at the same time broken the suction between the hull and the mud. After tensioning of the wires, the hull would be lifted clear of the sea bed by jacking the frame up its legs. The crane then moved the frame and hull underwater and lowered them over a shaped steel joist cradle. When the hull was resting on the cradle the whole assembly was lifted out of the water onto a barge for towage to Portsmouth Naval Base.

Recovery was achieved during 9–11 October 1982 and despite a small but spectacular failure of part of the frame the wreck was safely conveyed to No. 3 dock, where she was covered with an aluminium tent and sprayed with water continuously. Subsequently it has been rotated upright for further preservation work.

1. CROCKER R. J. and GRACE J. S. The recovery of the Mary Rose. *Struct. Engr*, 1984, **62A**, 57–63.

15. Haslar model testing tank for ship performance

A simple brick building at the Admiralty's Experimental Establishment, Haslar, Gosport, houses a concrete water tank 540 ft long, 20 ft wide and 7ft 9 in. deep, used for testing paraffin wax models of ships' hulls. The feasibility of predicting ship performance in this way had been

HEW 1600

SZ 614 987

proved in the mid-nineteenth century by William Froude and his work was continued by his son Robert Edmund, who designed the Haslar tank. William Froude worked for I. K. Brunel on the Bristol and Exeter Railway (HEW 1547, p.105) and other projected routes in Devon from 1837. He left in 1846 to concentrate on fluid mechanics research. Brunel encouraged him because of his own involvement in ship design and later asked him to investigate hull performance for the *Great Eastern*, 27 380 tons, launched in 1858.

Froude originally used a launch, loaned to him by G. P. Bidder, to tow his own yacht for experimental work but concluded that model testing would be more satisfactory. His theoretical work showed that a scale relationship could be established between model and prototype.[1] With Admiralty financial help he excavated a 250 ft canal near his house at Chelston Cross, Torquay (now a hotel) and began model testing in 1873. The models were towed by a carriage astride the canal running on rails and hauled by a steam winch.

William Froude died suddenly in 1879, but his son continued the work and, in 1884, persuaded the Admiralty that more refined facilities were needed. They built a new tank at Haslar under his superintendence. He designed all the equipment, including a lightweight travelling carriage, essentially two trusses of 2 in. square hollow timber members, those in tension having strained wire through them. The carriage ran on rails accurately set at a fixed distance above water level. Testing started in 1886.

Father and son between them presented many papers to the British Association, the Institution of Civil Engineers and the Royal Institute of Naval Architects. Both were elected Fellows of the Royal Society. By 1919, when Robert Froude retired, he had superintended the testing of over 250 000 models.

The technique of model testing was quickly seen to be applicable to many civil engineering problems involving river flood control, coastal erosion, accretion in navigable channels, etc. A model of the navigable channel of the River Garonne was built by Fargue in 1875, followed, in 1880, by one of the Mersey estuary to investigate the

Opposite: Nab Tower, Solent. Courtesy of *New Civil Engineer*

effect of building the Manchester Ship Canal (HEW 88),[2] superintended by Osborne Reynolds.

1. ABELL W. William Froude. *Trans Instn Nav. Archits*, 1934, **76**.

2. BARBEY M. F. *Civil engineering heritage: northern England*. Thomas Telford, London, 1981, 164–165.

16. Nab Tower, Solent ◆

During the 1914–18 war it was decided to sink a row of six anti-submarine towers across the Channel. The project was under the control of Alexander Gibb, The Admir-

HEW 1313

SZ 740 860

alty's Civil Engineer-in-Chief, and was designed by R. St. George Moore, who was responsible for Brighton Palace Pier (HEW 429, p.199). Construction was at Shoreham Harbour (HEW 1412 p.202) by a company of Royal Engineers.

One tower was nearly finished when the war ended, so it was modified to replace the Nab lightship at the eastern entrance to the Solent, to mark the edge of shallow water off the Isle of Wight. In September 1920 it was floated, towed to site and sunk on a prepared base, by flooding in 13 fathoms. A tilt of about 1 in 60 developed, but has remained constant.

The structure comprises three concentric steel cylinders of 8 ft, 30 ft and 55 ft diameter, 75 ft 8 in. high, tied to a four tier reinforced concrete pyramidal base of honeycomb construction, with a 6 ft module. The total height of the concrete base is 81 ft 10 in. For towing, the bottom tier, 194 ft long by 162 ft wide, acted as a raft divided into 18 water-tight compartments.

The space between the 8 ft and 30 ft diameter cylinders is divided into seven storeys, the bottom being the engine room, ventilated by the 8 ft shaft. Above are crew's quarters, store rooms, etc. The second storey from the top was plugged with concrete as a defence measure. The whole of the space between the 55 ft and 30 ft diameter cylinders down to seabed was also to be filled with concrete. The total height from seabed to the gun deck, now a helicopter landing pad, is 173 ft 6 in. The light is unattended.

♣

17. Ryde Pier, Isle of Wight

HEW 433

SZ 593 930

Ryde Pier,[1] 1740 ft long, was built by R. E. Cooper and opened in 1814, for the Portsmouth ferry service. It was the first major structure of this type in the United Kingdom. As ferry steamers became larger, it was extended from time to time, until 1842 when the head was built, making the total length 2250 ft.

One spur to the development of Ryde and its pier, was the frequent visits to Osborne House by Queen Victoria and Prince Albert. A two track tramway was added in 1864 on a separate structure alongside and between 1884 and 1890 both piers were reconstructed, using cast-iron columns and screw piles with wrought iron main beams and bracing. The tramway was standard gauge and horse-hauled until 1886, when the third rail electric traction was introduced, following the example of Volks Railway, Brighton (HEW 500, TQ 315 035 to 333 033) of 1883, which was 2 ft 9 in. gauge.

With the expansion of the Island's rail network and the opening of Ryde station in 1864, public pressure developed for a terminus at the pierhead. A two track jetty was constructed in 1879–80, with a track length over water of 2178 ft. It was founded on 45 trestles of Hughes piles, a 12 in. diameter wrought iron tube, with six longitudinal wrought iron fins riveted on externally; followed by 42 trestles on cast-iron screw piles with three sets of wings each, driven up to 50 ft penetration through quicksand. The timber decking was replaced by reinforced concrete in 1906.

In 1924 the Southern Railway took over the tramway system and in 1927 replaced the electric units by internal combustion engined vehicles, because the generating machinery was in poor condition. Thus ended Britain's first standard gauge electric railway.

By 1967 the railway system of the Island had been

Ryde Pier, Isle of Wight

reduced to a single route from Ryde Pier Head to Shanklin. The Southern Railway electrified the system and introduced ex-London Transport tube railway rolling stock. In 1969 the tram service was stopped and extra shuttle trains were provided. The tram pier was redecked for road vehicles, so that they no longer used the promenade section of the pier.

1. BLACKBURN A. and MACKETT J. *The railways and tramways of Ryde.* Town and Country Press, Bracknell, 1971.

18. The Needles Lighthouse

Lighthouses constructed to guard headlands, rather than isolated rocks (such as Bishop Rock, HEW 75, p.5), were generally sited on a promontory but frequently obstruction by low cloud compelled the later construction of a lighthouse at sea-level. This happened at The Needles, Beachy Head (HEW 77, p.213), and St Catherine's Point (HEW 736). Trinity House started the replacement process in 1853 at the Needles, by briefing their Consulting Engineer, James Walker. He recommended that the 1786 lighthouse should be replaced by siting a new one at sea-level just west of the chalk stacks.

Sea lighthouses traditionally have the shape of a tree trunk in elevation, a shape originated by John Smeaton at Eddystone in 1759 (HEW 73, p.48). But James Walker designed a vertical tower, 72 ft 6 in. high to gallery and 21 ft diameter.

The tower was constructed on a masonry faced concrete base of 38 ft diameter founded in the chalk 4 ft below low water. At the tower base there is a plinth with stepped stones recessed on their top surface for vertical keying. Above the solid plinth the tower masonry is 3 ft 6 in. thick at the base, tapering to 2 ft thick at the top, with a course height of 1 ft 9 in. Keying between courses is by a groove in the top and bottom of each stone, forming a circle round the tower, filled with cement. This was a departure from the traditional method of keying the masonry blocks together both horizontally and vertically.

There are five internal floors, supported on two concentric rings of wrought iron joists, intersected by eight radial joists built into the walls. A 23 ft diameter balcony

with solid parapet surmounts the tower and supports an octagonal lantern housing a 35 000 candlepower light with its focal plane 80 ft above high tide level. Construction began in 1855; the light was first lit in 1859.

Needles
Lighthouse

167

St. Catherine's Lighthouse

19. St Catherine's Lighthouse, Isle of Wight

♣

HEW 736

SZ 495 772

As a result of its height, St Catherine's lighthouse has frequently proved ineffective because of low cloud. It was sited on St Catherine's Hill, ¾ mile inland and 750 ft above sea- level.

Shipwrecks were not uncommon at St Catherine's Point; one in 1314 involved a cargo of fine wine belonging to the Ecclesiastical authorities.[1] The crew sold the wine to the local people including the landowner Walter de Godeton. A year later this was discovered. There were legal proceedings and De Godeton was ordered to pay the consignees. Also the Pope ordered him, on threat of excommunication, to construct an oratory, where a priest would chant orations for drowned sailors and a light tower which was to be tended by the priest. By 1328 he had completed the building.

Only the elegant tower remains. It is octagonal in plan externally, square internally, 32 ft 6 in. high, 10 ft wide with four counterforts taken up to half height. The light was set within a ring of eight small openings about 1 ft 3 in. wide. It is a Scheduled Ancient Monument.

Trinity House built a replacement in 1785 but that also was too high and was replaced by the present lighthouse in 1838 (SZ 489 753), about 100 yd from the sea and 30 ft above high tide. Even so, that also was shortened later in the nineteenth century.

1. STONE P. G. The oratory of St Catherine. *The architectural antiquities of the Isle of Wight*. Part II. The west Medina, 1891, 27–29.

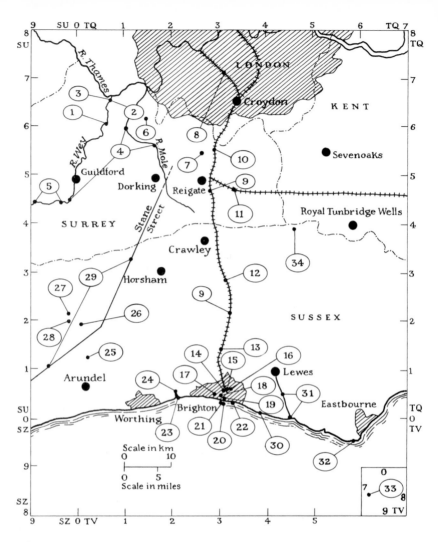

1. Wey Navigation
2. Brooklands Motor Race Track
3. Cast-iron Bridge, Weybridge
4. Godalming, Cobham and
   Leatherhead Bridge
5. Upper Wey Ancient Bridges
6. Oxshott Footbridge
7. Reigate Hill Footbridge
8. Surrey Iron Railway
9. London to Brighton Railway
10. Mertsham Tunnels
11. Bletchingley Tunnel

12. Ouse Viaduct, Balcombe
13. Clayton Tunnel
14. New England Road Bridges
15. Brighton Station
16. London Road Viaduct
17. Brighton Water Supply
18. Brighton Main Drainage
19. Brighton Pavillion and Dome
20. Brighton Chain Pier
21. West and Palace Piers
22. Brighton Marina
23. Shoreham Harbour

24. Shoreham Trestle Bridge
25. Timberley Viaduct
26. Stopham Ancient Bridge
27. Petworth Park Dam
28. Petworth Water Supply
29. Stane Street
30. Cliff Stabilisation, East of Brighton
31. Newhaven Harbour and Lower Ouse
    Navigation
32. Beachy Head Lighthouse
33. Royal Sovereign Lighthouse
34. Roman Road, Holtye

7. Sussex and South Surrey

The area's topography is dominated by the chalk downlands, which have been obstacles to road and rail routes. Although there are identifiable east–west transport routes across the region, both along the coast and further inland, the north–south routes connecting the coastal urban conurbations, especially Brighton, with London tend to dominate. This is seen in the quality of the mainly dualled A24 road from Worthing to Dorking and the M23–A23 route to Brighton. A major Roman route, Stane Street, was designed to connect London to Chichester in the region's south-west corner and part of a north–south Roman route has been found at Holtye, East Sussex.

Canal and training works tended to serve local rather than regional needs and are illustrated by the Wey Navigation, designed to connect Guildford with the Thames. Another example is the development of the lower Ouse, designed both to enable shipping to reach Lewes and to improve drainage.

Railways ultimately provided an extensive regional network, with the London to Brighton route being of greatest importance. However, the world's first public railway, the Surrey Iron Railway, was built under Parliamentary powers obtained in 1801. The area's topography required a number of impressive railway structures, including the iron Timberley Viaduct over the Arun and the 37-span brick Ouse Viaduct at Balcombe on the London to Brighton route. Other notable railway features include the 27-span London Road Viaduct at Brighton, an early reinforced concrete footbridge at Oxshott and the Bletchingley and Clayton Tunnels.

The mid-nineteenth century was a time when numerous water supply and sewerage schemes were constructed in Britain's expanding urban areas in response to major public health problems. Such works are typified by those at Brighton which involved both Thomas Hawksley and John Hawkshaw, eminent Victorian sanitary engineers. Older water supply schemes are illustrated by the Petworth supply and its associated Beam pump at Coultershaw. In the same area is the Petworth Dam built to provide an ornamental lake under the direction of Capability Brown.

The area's coastline, which largely comprises a shallow bay between Selsey Bill and Beachy Head, is punctuated by a number of rivers. The Adur and Ouse have the relatively small ports of Shoreham and Newhaven at their mouths, both of which required the stabilisation of the river's entrance to the sea before they could be developed. Littoral drift,which caused the estuaries to move eastwards, has contributed to many other coast erosion problems along the shoreline and necessitated the construction of substantial lengths of sea wall as part of cliff stabilisation works to the east of Brighton. Other maritime works include the off-shore Royal Sovereign and Beachy Head lighthouses, the relatively recent Brighton Marina and Brighton's seaside piers. Also in Brighton is the distinctive Royal Pavilion complex developed for King George IV when he was Prince of Wales.

Wey Navigation,
Walsham Lock
Gates

1. Wey Navigation

♣

HEW 1532

SU 975 441 to
TQ 076 659

To reduce the cost of sending timber and grain to London, and coal delivery to Guildford, the town corporation in 1621 and 1624 petitioned Parliament for the River Wey to be made navigable from the Thames to Guildford, some 15 miles. The work,[1] which involved 9 miles of cut, 50 ft wide and 4 ft deep, and 12 locks, with a total rise of 80 ft, was completed and opened in 1653. The locks had battered turf sides and could accept 80 ton barges. At Guildford Wharf a wooden treadmill crane (HEW 1468, SU 994 495) was installed. This could lift 2 tons and has been restored.

In 1760 a 4 mile extension to Godalming, planned by John Smeaton,[2] was approved by Parliament. The work, opened in 1764, included four locks with a rise of 32 ft and a minimum channel depth of 3 ft. After the opening of the Woking to Guildford branch of the London and South Western Railway in 1845 the navigation went into decline.

In 1821 the keeper at Thames lock was William Stevens, whose descendants were eventually to become owners of the navigation. In 1969 Henry Stevens gave the navigation to the National Trust. Traffic is now confined to pleasure craft.

1. HADFIELD C. *The canals of south and south east England.* David and Charles, Newton Abbot, 1969, 118–124 and 372–373.

2. SKEMPTON A. W. (ed.). *John Smeaton, F.R.S.* Thomas Telford, London, 1981, 109.

2. Brooklands Motor Race Track

♦

HEW 1428

TQ 066 623

The development of the automobile in Britain owes much to the initiative of H. F. Locke-King, who built at Brooklands the world's first track intended exclusively for motor racing and testing. It was opened in 1907.

The track was 2¾ miles long, pear-shaped in plan, with a minimum radius of 1000 ft. The surface was formed in 6 in. thick unreinforced concrete laid in 10 ft wide strips. Imported filling was needed to complete the embankments, which had a maximum superelevation of 29 ft on the 100 ft wide track. Maximum crossfall was 1

Brooklands Race
Track

in 2 at the outer edge. The designer was A. W. Donaldson, MICE, and the main Contractor Price and Reeves.[1,2]

Where the curved track crossed the River Wey there was a reinforced concrete bridge designed by L. G. Mouchel on the Hennebique system. This had five spans of about 36 ft on the outer diameter, the longitudinal beams having arched soffits with a 3 ft 6 in. rise. The structure was supported on reinforced concrete piles generally 14 in. square.

Shortly after opening, the world 24 hour record was raised above 65 miles/h. In 1908 100 miles/h was exceeded for the first time. By 1929 British cars had established a world reputation for reliability. The lap record of 143 miles/h was made in 1935. The track closed on the outbreak of the Secod World War in 1939.

The area inside the track was developed as an airfield and contained the Vickers aircraft factory. Vimy twin engined bombers were built there and one of these was the first aeroplane to fly the Atlantic non-stop, in 1919. In the Second World War the Wellington bomber, with its geodetic construction, was designed at Brooklands by Barnes Wallis.

1. New works in concrete at home and abroad. *Concrete and Constructional Engineering*, 1907–8, **2**, 240–243 and 328.

2. TWELVETREES W. N. Some engineering features of the Brooklands motor track. *Engineering Review*, 1907, **16**, 311–316.

3. Weybridge Cast-iron Arch Bridge

The first reference to a bridge at this point, where an ancient east–west route crossed the River Wey, was in 675 AD. A timber structure was replaced by the present bridge in 1865. It has three spans of 43 ft 6 in., with a total length of 183 ft. Each span has six cast-iron arch ribs cast in three sections, the arch rise being 5 ft. The spandrels are open, having verticals cast integrally with the arch ribs which have the founder's name 'Joseph Hamblet, Oldbury', displayed. Design was by C. H. Howell, County Surveyor of Surrey.

The road width is 19 ft 1 in., with a 5 ft 3 in. footway on one side. The parapets are cast-iron fences with verticals, supported at intervals by elegant hoops.

In 1945 a new bridge was built 50 yd downstream, carrying the A317 Weybridge to Chertsey road and taking most of the traffic.

HEW 1427

TQ 069 647

4. Godalming Bridge, Cobham Bridge and Leatherhead Bridge

There were bridges at these sites in medieval times and apparently they were in need of replacement simultaneously, as an authorising Act of Parliament was passed in 1782. The new bridge designs were made by the County Surveyor of Surrey, George Gwilt, and construction was placed with one contractor, George Fentiman. All the bridges were to be of red brickwork finished with Portland stone cappings and string courses. Godalming and Cobham also shared an attractive design of refuge. These are semicircular in plan and are supported on trumpet-shaped smooth stone corbels.

Godalming bridge, over the Wey, has five segmental arches varying from 12 ft 10 in. to 14 ft 10 in. span. In 1930 it was widened to 36 ft, the new arch extensions being in reinforced concrete, with facing brickwork to match the old work. Traffic over it has been much lighter since the diversion of the A3 Portsmouth road to the west of Godalming in 1934.

Cobham Bridge, on the Mole, has nine brick arches, with spans varying from 12 ft 3 in. to 15 ft 6 in. It has been

Godalming Bridge:
HEW 1426
SU 974 442

Cobham Bridge:
HEW 1425
TQ 098 605

Leatherhead Bridge:
HEW 1424
TQ 163 563

175

Cobham Bridge

widened twice, from 25 ft to 40 ft in 1915, then to 50 ft in 1951. Traffic has been reduced following diversion of the A3 Portsmouth road to the west of Cobham in the mid-1970s. It now carries the A245, Leatherhead to Byfleet road.

Leatherhead Bridge, also over the Mole, is the longest of the three, with an overall length of 312 ft. It has 14 equal segmental three ring brick arches of 13 ft 4 in. span and corbelled refuges. Traffic between Leatherhead and Guildford is now restricted to one-way working.

5. Upper Wey Ancient Bridges: Unstead, Eashing, Somerset, Elstead, Tilford, South-East and Tilford, North-West

The River Wey's upper reaches between Godalming and Farnham were crossed by fourteen medieval bridges of which six have survived.[1,2] A number have been substantially repaired. They are thought to date from the early thirteenth century when they were probably constructed by Cistercian Monks who established Waverley Abbey in 1128. Local undressed Bargate stone was generally used, giving a rugged and functional appearance. The largest

Eashing Bridge

span, on Eashing Bridge, is around 15 ft and the low masonry arches are normally semicircular in shape. The bridges are all around 12 ft wide.

Unstead Bridge now conveys an 8 ft 9 in. asphalt carriageway between iron balustrades over its five arches, giving a total length of around 100 ft. One of its arches has substantial brickwork repairs and is largely buried in the bank. There are pointed cutwaters on the upstream side, but none downstream.

Eashing Bridge, once thought to be a continuous multi-span structure is now in two sections, separated by a central island between the river Wey and a mill stream. Four spans are visible to the north over a length of about 65 ft and three to the south cover about 55 ft. Several courses of brickwork are visible above the masonry structure and there are no parapets, only timber rails. There are pointed cutwaters upstream and rounded ones downstream. The bridge was repaired in 1900 by the Society for the Protection of Ancient Buildings.

The 71 ft long Somerset Bridge has four spans and pointed cutwaters on both sides which are largely encased in relatively recently laid concrete. Only one of the central arches appears to be the original construction of flat undressed slabs. Another arch is of brick construction dating from repair work in 1826. Further substantial

Unstead:
HEW 1797
SU 993 454

Eashing:
HEW 1480
SU 946 438

Somerset:
HEW 1796
SU 922 439

Elstead:
HEW 1795
SU 905 438

Tilford,
South-East:
HEW 1794
SU 874 434

Tilford,
North-West:
HEW 1793
SU 872 435

177

Elstead Bridge

brickwork, including the parapets, is seen over the masonry arches.

Elstead Bridge has five spans over a 180 ft length. Further spans probably extend into the banks. Like Eashing Bridge, the cutwaters are pointed upstream and rounded on the other side, and, like Somerset Bridge, there is substantial brickwork including parapets above the masonry.

There are two bridges at Tilford. The south-eastern, nearly 190 ft long is of seven spans but one of brickwork is separated from the masonry arches by an extended pier. Two arches are partially buried in the other bank. The brick and the first masonry arch are of elliptical shape, the others are semicircular. Again there are pointed cutwaters upstream and rounded downstream. Timber parapet rails are supported on a series of timber joists cantilevering from the bridge sides. The north-eastern bridge is more modest, being only around 100 ft long over five masonry arches. It has similar cutwaters and timber rails and carries west-bound traffic only. An adjacent, recently constructed, reinforced concrete bridge carries east-bound and all heavy traffic.

Eashing, Elstead and the two Tilford Bridges are all Grade I Listed Structures, Unstead and Somerset are Grade II*. All are Scheduled Ancient Monuments.

1. Renn D. F. The river Wey bridges between Farnham and Guildford. Tilford Bridge
Surrey Archaelogical Society Research, 1974, **1**, 78–82.

2. Jervoise E. *The ancient bridges of the South of England.* Architectural Press, London, 1930, 22–26.

6. Sheath Lane Railway Footbridge, Oxshott

Railway footbridges at stations and for public footpaths became common in the 1860s. Many such examples in cast iron and wrought iron still exist. Early in the twentieth century, reinforced concrete structures, as at Oxshott, began to appear. It was built in 1909 and designed by L. G. Mouchel using the Hennebique system of reinforced concrete, to the requirements of J. W. Jacomb Hood, Chief Engineer of the London and South Western Railway.

HEW 1455

TQ 139 606

The bridge spans 44 ft 10 in. over two running lines and a siding. Solid 6 in. thick parapets, panelled to 4 in., form the main beams. The bridge width is 4 ft 6 in. between parapets and is still in use and in very good condition.

From this was developed a standard precast reinforced concrete footbridge design, used extensively by the Southern Railway and in other Railway regions after nationalisation. Examples of this design, presenting an almost identical appearance to the Sheath Lane Bridge, were still being built 50 years later.

7. Reigate Hill Footbridge

♣

HEW 1423

TQ 263 523

In 1825 the steep hill up the North Downs scarp out of Reigate on the turnpike road to Sutton, now A217, was eased by the excavation of a 30 ft deep cutting through the chalk. This severed the ancient trackway along the edge of the scarp from Guildford to Canterbury known as the Pilgrims' Way. A chain suspension footbridge was erected, but by 1908 corrosion made replacement necessary.

L. G. Mouchel prepared plans for a reinforced concrete arch bridge on the Hennebique system. There are two 9 in. wide by 15 in. deep arch ribs 65 ft 6 in. long with an 8 ft rise, at 7 ft 3 in. centres springing from the cutting sides. They support an open-spandrel reinforced concrete deck with cast-iron railings on either side of the 7 ft footway. The bridge was opened in 1910 and is still in very good condition, though it has required substantial repairs on several occasions.

The same road, about 1½ miles further south, at TQ 253 503, passes through a tunnel 56 yd long, constructed in 1823 under the private estate of Earl Sommers. Between brick walls it is 20 ft wide, including a 3 ft wide footway. Tolls were originally charged, but were discontinued in 1856.

8. The Surrey Iron Railway and Croydon Merstham and Godstone Railway

♠

HEW 1387

TQ 255 752 to
318 656 and
298 538

By 1800 Croydon had become a thriving industrial and agricultural centre in urgent need of better goods access to London than the road system allowed. There were 200 water-wheels on some 90 sites in the River Wandle valley, between Croydon and the Thames at Wandsworth which contributed to the area's importance.[1]

In 1799 local industrialists asked William Jessop to

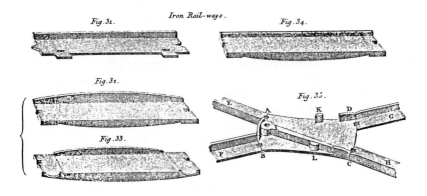

Iron Rail-ways.

Fig. 31. Fig. 34. Fig. 32. Fig. 35. Fig. 33.

plan a canal down the valley. He reported it to be feasible but impracticable because the only source of feeder water was the river and its use would deprive the mills of their power source. He suggested, instead, an iron plate railway. This proposal was accepted, he prepared plans and Royal Assent was given in 1801 to the Surrey Iron Railway Act, which also included a branch to Carshalton and a basin at Wandsworth.

Details from Surrey Iron Railway

Unlike other early railways, built on private land and carrying only the owner's goods, this was a public railway, the first in the world, on land acquired under the Act. The railway company only provided the track; wagons were owned by others, who conveyed merchandise for the public, on payment of tolls.

The Surrey Iron Railway (SIR) was a double track plateway using cast-iron L-shaped rails, 3 ft long, with the vertical flange on the inside, set to give a gauge of 4 ft 2 in. between the flange's outer faces. Crossovers were formed from hinged flanges. The wagons had flat-tyred wheels, making them usable on roads. A horse could haul five loaded 3 ton wagons on the flat.

The earthworks and bridging required were minimal, so the railway was quickly built and came into operation in 1803. Its length from Wandsworth to Croydon was 8½ miles and the Carshalton branch 1¼ miles.

Jessop had foreseen in his first report that the SIR might be the first link in a longer railway, possibly as far as the south coast. In 1802, its promoters decided to get Jessop and others to survey a route to Reigate, with a branch to Godstone. The Croydon, Merstham and Godstone Railway Act was passed in 1803 but because of financial difficulties and inflation, only 8¾ miles were built, to Merstham, where there were quarries which could supply London builders with stone from the Upper Greensand and high quality hydraulic lime from the chalk of the North Downs.[2]

The line, opened in 1805, climbed almost all the way from Croydon to Merstham with a ruling gradient of about 1 in 100. It required appreciable earthworks, including a 30 ft deep cutting north of Merstham and a 20 ft embankment with an arch over the Chipstead Valley road at TQ 294 594. Remains of these are to be seen, including parapets of two bridges over the cutting, which have been filled in, south of Hooley at TQ 288 556 and TQ 288 558.

The Contractor for the whole of the Croydon Merstham and Godstone Railway (CMGR), including the manufacture of the rails and the supply of materials, equipment and labour, was the Butterley Company which was an early example of a single firm acting as a general contractor for a large construction project.

The CMGR was closed in 1839 and its land was purchased by the London and Brighton Railway (HEW 1573) for use, in part, of its alignment. By 1846, traffic on the SIR had diminished so much that it was sold, partly to local landowners and partly to the London, Brighton and South Coast Railway for use on a new line between Wimbledon and Croydon.

Apart from the remains of earthworks and bridges mentioned above, little is visible on the site of either the SIR or the CMGR. There is a stack of some 40 stone sleepers in a park at Carshalton (TQ 282 648), two lengths of track are displayed in Quality Street, Merstham (TQ 290 533) and the Science Museum has a length of rail. Between Mitcham (TQ 275 680) and Beddington (TQ 283

672) is Tramway Path, along the line of the Carshalton branch and nearby, at TQ 275 682, a short road named Jeppos Lane, perhaps a transposition of letters from 'Jessop'.

1. BAYLISS D. A. *Retracing the first public railway*. Living History Publications, Croydon, 1981.

2. HADFIELD C. and SKEMPTON A. W. *William Jessop, Engineer*. David and Charles, Newton Abbot, 1979, 175–180.

9. The London to Brighton Railway ♠

In the mid 1830s, various proposals were made to connect London by rail with the south coast. In section 5, p.151 the development of the London to Southampton route is described. Next in importance were links to Dover, for the cross-channel trade, and Brighton, then developing rapidly as a seaside resort.

HEW 1573

TQ 330 800 to

From an early stage, there was parliamentary pressure for a common route to be found out of London to the south side of the North Downs, from the London and Greenwich Railway's terminus at London Bridge, over their lines as far as Corbett's Lane, Bermondsey and thence over the London and Croydon Railway. These two lines were then under construction.

The South-Eastern Railway (SER) (HEW 1448, p.229), received its Act in June 1836 for a line to Dover from an end-on connection with the London and Croydon, crossing the Downs at Oxted before turning east for Tonbridge and Folkestone. However, work through the Downs was suspended after the London and Brighton Railway Act was passed in July 1837, until a final common route, proposed by Sir John Rennie, was agreed for the line to leave the London and Croydon at Norwood Junction and cross the North Downs between Coulsdon and Merstham, to Redhill (TQ 281 505), where the South-Eastern would turn east. A split in ownership of this section was made, the London and Brighton (LBR) retaining the northern end, to Stoat's Nest, Coulsdon, and the South-Eastern buying the southern half, to Redhill. Each company had free running powers over the other's line.

John Urpeth Rastrick and David Mocatta were appointed Engineer and Architect to the LBR. Construction of the line started near Merstham in July 1838 and it was opened through to Brighton in September 1841.[1]

Despite the hilly route, gradients were limited to 1 in 264 and curves were not severe. Four tunnels were needed, Merstham (HEW 1520), Balcombe (TQ 292 326 to TQ 296 316), Clayton (HEW 503) and Patcham (TQ 297 091 to TQ 298 086). Earthworks exceeded 6 million yd.[3] A fine viaduct (HEW 33) crosses the valley of the River Ouse near Balcombe.

In 1846 the LBR and London and Croydon Railways amalgamated to form the London, Brighton and South Coast Railway (LBSCR). The LBR had already acquired the Brighton and Chichester and Brighton, Lewes and Hastings Railways, which had been promoted by them, designed by Rastrick and Mocatta and opened in succession in 1845 and 1846.

By the early 1850s the LBSCR, the SER and the East Kent Railway (later the London, Chatham and Dover), were pressing to extend their lines to the West End. The LBSCR were the first to achieve this objective, in 1860, with the opening of their portion of Victoria Station, connected to the original line at Norwood Junction. By this time they also owned a section of London Bridge Station and separate tracks out to Bermondsey.

As traffic increased, so did congestion on the section between Norwood Junction and Redhill, shared between the LBSCR and the SER, particularly after the opening of the SER line to Guildford and Reading in 1849. This congestion was eased by the opening in 1868 of the Sevenoaks cut-off between New Cross and Tonbridge, which took virtually all the SER's through traffic to Kent; but the LBSCR's traffic continued to grow and by the early 1890s it was decided to build a new double track line from Coulsdon to Earlswood Junction, 1 mile south of Redhill, bypassing Merstham and Redhill stations. This became known as the Quarry Line, passing close by the quarries previously served by the Croydon, Merstham and Godstone Railway. The line involved a second tunnel at Merstham (HEW 1635) and a short one taking the line under Redhill town and the SER line to Tonbridge. The line is more heavily graded than the original railway, rising at 1 in 165 to the north portal of the

Merstham tunnel and then falling at an average of about 1 in 200 to the south portal of Redhill tunnel. The Quarry Line was authorised in 1894 and opened in November 1899, thus for the first time giving the LBSCR a line of their own all the way to Brighton.

1. TURNER J. H. *The London Brighton and South Coast Railway.* Batsford, London, 1977.

10. Merstham Old Tunnel and Merstham Quarry Line Tunnel

Merstham old tunnel[1] takes the length of track owned originally by the South Eastern Railway (HEW 1448, p.229) through the North Downs. The route took advantage of the Merstham gap, but even so a tunnel 1 mile 71 yd long was required through the chalk scarp.

Merstham Old Tunnel:
HEW 1530
TQ 288 558 to 291 542

The tunnel is straight and virtually level, at the summit of 1 in 264 gradients on both approaches. It is 23 ft both in height and width, horseshoe shaped and brick-lined throughout. The ends were driven from cuttings between 70 and 80 ft deep and there were ten intermediate shafts.

Merstham Quarry Line Tunnel:
HEW 1635
TQ 289 558 to 292 539

With the other tunnels on the London to Brighton line (HEW 1573), Merstham was whitewashed inside and gas lit, to allay the public's fear of the dark at a time when open coaches were still in use.

Quarry tunnel,[1] as it is usually known, 100 yd east of, and roughly parallel to, Merstham old tunnel, is longer, at 1 mile 353 yd. It falls from the northern portal at a continuous gradient of 1 in 206. It is generally similar in construction to the old tunnel, with six working shafts.

BLOWER A. *British railway tunnels.* Ian Allan, London, 1964, 55, 69 and 70.

11. Bletchingley Tunnel

After the South-Eastern Railway (SER) (HEW 1448, p.229) turned away east from the London to Brighton line at Redhill, it had a reasonably easy route through the Weald, mainly on a series of low embankments, to a point midway between Ashford and Folkestone. The only exception was at Bletchingley,[1,2] some 4 miles out from

HEW 1531

TQ 333 487 to 345 486

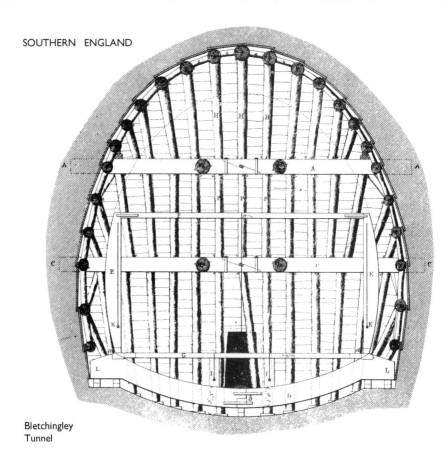

Bletchingley
Tunnel

Tunnelling
technique

Redhill, where a tunnel had to be driven through a mixture of clay and fissured water-bearing shale.

Bletchingley tunnel is 1327 yd long, straight, horseshoe shaped and fully brick-lined. To deal with the shale, close boarding and elaborate shoring was needed and work was limited to 12 ft lengths. The bricks were made on site, without frogs to save on the cement mortar in which the brickwork was set. Twelve working shafts were used.

The tunnel was whitewashed throughout, following the practice of the London and Brighton Railway (HEW 1573). It was designed by the SER's Chief Engineer, William Cubitt, and built by direct labour, supervised by Frederick W. Simms as Resident Engineer. Construction was completed in 1842.

1. SIMMS F. W. *Practical tunnelling.* Crosby Lockwood, London, 1844.

2. BLOWER A. *British railway tunnels.* Ian Allan, London, 1964, 82 and 83.

12. Ouse Viaduct, Balcombe   ♣

This is the most impressive structure on the London to Brighton main line (HEW 1573), and one of the most elegant viaducts ever built.[1] It is 1475 ft long, straight, and has a maximum height of 96 ft above the River Ouse. There are thirty-seven 30 ft span semicircular red brick arches. The piers are tapered in the side and end elevations, and have deep vertical voids about 10 ft wide in the centre, virtually forming two piers. At the top and bottom the voids are closed by six-ring semicircular brick arches. This weight-saving method creates an attractive slender appearance.

HEW 33

TQ 322 280 to 323 277

The parapets are of classical balustrading in Caen stone, which is also used for string courses, pier caps and four small Italianate pavilions at each end of the viaduct. Refuges are corbelled over each pier. All materials were brought along the upper Ouse navigation.

The designers of this viaduct and other major works on the line were the Company's Engineer and Architect, J. U. Rastrick and D. Mocatta.

TURNER J. H. *The London Brighton and South Coast Railway.* Batsford, London, 1977, **1**, 124.

♦ 13. Clayton Tunnel

HEW 503

TQ 293 126 to 297 141

Clayton Tunnel takes the London and Brighton Railway (HEW 1573) through the South Downs. On either side it is approached by 1 in 264 gradients the summit of which is at the south portal. It is straight, 1 mile 499 yd long and lined with five rings of brickwork. Eleven working shafts were constructed, the deepest being 270 ft.

The much illustrated north portal is embellished with twin castellated turrets. The effect is spoiled by a cottage perched incongruously behind the portals above the tunnel crown. This is a relic of the days when the tunnel was gas lit. The cottage housed the plant attendant.

♣ 14. Railway Bridges over New England Road: Montpelier Bridge and Goods Yard Line

Montpelier Bridge:
HEW 1416
TQ 308 053 to
309 054

Goods Yard Line:
HEW 493
TQ 310 054

The London to Brighton Railway (HEW 1573) crosses New England Road about 300 yd north of Brighton Station.[1] The first section of the bridge, built for the opening of the line in 1841, was a handsome yellow brick struc-

ture, having a 22 ft semicircular arch span and 6 ft pedestrian arches on either side. The overall width of the bridge was 32 ft.

In 1847 the Brighton locomotive works were inaugurated, in a rather congested site east of the main line and between New England Road and the terminus. They expanded rapidly and by 1853 were being extended westwards, making it necessary to move the running lines onto a new extension of the bridge. This was supported by four Warren trusses at 8 ft 9 in. centres. These were among the earliest such trusses to be used in Britain and were unusual in that all the diagonal members were in cast iron. In 1864 these were strengthened by the addition of wrought iron flat plates, pinned to the original cast-iron members.

Already as a result of the removal of the engine running and the carriage sheds from the locomotive works to the west side of the main line, the bridge had been extended further. This was done during the 1860s in three stages, all on wrought iron girders, giving a total bridge width of about 240 ft. In 1891, after the collapse of a cast-iron bridge at Norwood Junction, the Warren trusses were replaced by steel girders.

Top left: Ouse Viaduct

Top right: Clayton Tunnel

189

After the Warren truss extension, the original brick arch bridge only conveyed sidings leading from the locomotive works and these sidings were removed after closure of the works in 1970. The structure remains unused. In 1984, the three extensions nearest the original arch were regirdered in steel with a reinforced concrete deck.

Brighton goods yard was also south of New England Road, east of the station and at a lower level. Originally the only rail access was from the Shoreham line, by a tunnel through the chalk fill under the station. To reduce shunting movements, a direct approach line was constructed, crossing New England Road, about 80 yd east of the original brick arch bridge. An elegant cast-iron structure was erected in 1852. It has four arch ribs, each cast in three sections, with integral vertical spandrel members provided by the Regent Foundry, Brighton. The bridge was further strengthened in later years by the insertion of three steel plate girders under the tracks. Here again, the goods yard has been closed. The bridge remains but is unused.

1. ROLT L. T. C. *Red for danger*. Pan Books, London, 1966, 105.

♣

HEW 435

TQ 310 050

15. Brighton Station

For the original Brighton station of 1841, David Mocatta designed the entrance building and J. U. Rastrick the timber trussed train shed.[1] At first this consisted of three bays and a fourth was added in 1861. These averaged 56 ft in width. In 1882–83, there were major alterations. Rastrick's roof was replaced by two main bays spanning 112 ft and a shorter bay of 46 ft span on the east side. The bay roofs are ridged and supported by wrought iron trusses, of which the bottom chords are elliptical in shape. The visual impression is enhanced by the fact that the 600 ft long shed is on a curve of about 1000 ft radius.

The trusses are supported on elaborate fluted cast-iron columns at about 30 ft centres which have moulded square plinths, displaying Brighton Corporation's coat of arms and with a classical cap. Lattice girders, supported on cast-iron angle brackets, with the London Brighton and South Coast Railway coat of arms incorporated, pro-

Brighton Station roof

vide longitudinal stability for the columns. The roof was designed by H. E. Wallis, the company's engineer.

At the same time a *porte-cochère*, in glass and iron, was added to the frontage. This has largely hidden Mocatta's work, though the arched windows and doorways at ground level can still be seen, together with the upper part of the frontage and the train shed roof.

1. TURNER J. T. H. *The London Brighton and South Coast Railway.* **3**. Batsford, London, 1979, 109, 133.

16. London Road Viaduct, Brighton ♣

This tall red brick viaduct dominates a residential area of east Brighton. It carries two tracks of the London Brighton and South Coast Railway (HEW 1573) to Lewes, on a curving branch east from the main London line, at a height of 67 ft above street level. The viaduct is 1170 ft long, with twenty-six 30 ft span semicircular arches and one 50 ft semi-elliptical arch over Preston Road. To main-

HEW 491

TQ 309 056

London Road
Viaduct

tain a constant arch span, the piers are tapered in elevation and, as on the Ouse Viaduct (HEW 33), have deep vertical voids in the centre, about 10 ft wide.

Cornices and parapets are in Caen stone and there are refuges over each pier. The tracks are carried on five two-ring brick, 4 ft span, semicircular longitudinal jack arches.

The structure was opened in 1846.[1] On 25 May 1943 a 1000 lb bomb destroyed pier 7, felling arches 7 and 8. The line was reopened on 12 October 1943.[2]

1. TURNER J. H. *The London Brighton and South Coast Railway.* **1.** Batsford, London, 1977, 218.

2. TOMS A. H. Repairs to railway viaduct over London Road, Brighton. *J. Instn Civ. Engrs*, 1945, **24**, 367.

♦

17. Brighton Water Supply

HEW 505

TQ 286 066

Brighton expanded rapidly in Victorian times and, in comparison with many large towns, the provision of water was not difficult, because it was situated on a vast area of chalk.

Thomas Hawksley was asked to prepare a water scheme for Brighton and Hove. He reported in 1858, recommending a site at Goldstone Bottom on the north west outskirts of Brighton, where test bores revealed a basin in the chalk. A deep bore-hole would be sunk, with adits running north and west. The water would be pumped to the surface by steam.[1]

A contract was placed with Easton Amos and Sons for a 120 h.p. compound beam engine with three Lancashire boilers. This would pump 120 000 gallons per hour against a head of 250 ft, from a 160 ft deep, 12 ft by 9 ft oval well, using two 33 in. bore by 30 in. stroke bucket pumps. A separate small high pressure pump was to deliver to the highest areas.

The machinery was housed in a fine ornate poly-chrome brick pumping station, with a dominating chim-

Goldstone
Pumping Station

ney. The building was planned to become symmetrical when doubled in size. This became necessary when the decision was taken to supply surrounding villages. In 1876 the extension was completed, with a 250 h.p. compound beam engine by the same firm, then called Easton and Anderson, capable of pumping 150 000 gallons per hour. Both engines are unique in the South of England. The beam engines were replaced by electric submersible pumps in 1952.

A private trust, called the Brighton and Hove Engineerium, took over the installation, repaired the building, replaced boilers and restored No. 2 engine and then No. 1 engine. Both engines are now used for steam demonstrations. The remainder of the premises have been converted into a museum illustrating the history of steam power in all its applications, even to balloons. A similar pumping station has been preserved at Eastney, Portsmouth (HEW 504, p.156).

1. MINNS J. Goldstone pumping station. *Brighton and Sussex Industrial History*, 1976, 7, 35.

18. Brighton and Hove Main Drainage

♦

HEW 499

TQ 280 045
TO 393 013

By 1850 the population of Brighton was over 40 000. Rapid expansion of speculative housing, with no drainage, caused pollution of wells by sewage percolating through the chalk, which contributed to a death rate which was typical of Victorian towns and cities. Beaches were polluted by pipes discharging crude sewage, and the Wellesbourne stream, piped in 1780 and flowing over the beach at the Palace Pier (HEW 429), was a main sewer. Yet, despite criticism in the national press and in *The Lancet*, the Council did not act until 1868, when they appointed Sir John Hawkshaw to report.[1]

His scheme involved construction of an intercepting sewer running eastwards from the west boundary of Hove to a ¼ mile long sea outfall at Portobello, 6 miles east of Brighton. Main sewers were to be provided running down London Road, Lewes Road and Marine Parade. All these sewers were 7 or 8 ft diameter, and on a fall of 3 ft per mile. A storm water overflow weir 72 ft long

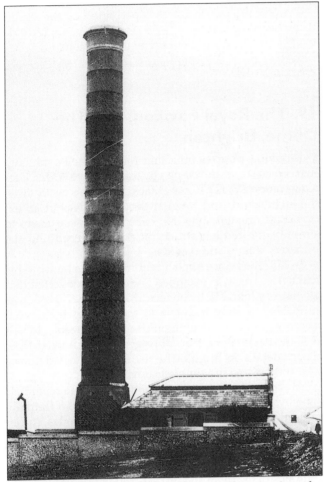

Brighton
Drainage,
Roedean
ventilation shaft ,
demolished 1933

was to be installed near Palace Pier, discharging into the sea with the Wellesbourne stream.

A contract was placed with Aird and Company in 1871 and the work was completed in 1874. The sewers were brick lined, using Burgess Hill yellow bricks and the sewer intersection show a high standard of workmanship.

Hawkshaw had overestimated future population increases in designing for 15 million gallons per day, so the system is still working within capacity. The sea outfall has, however, been extended to 1¼ miles. The storm water overflow weir has been lengthened to 98 ft.

195

Periodically public access is permitted up the storm-water overflow at Palace Pier on fine evenings at low tide to view the main weir and sewer intersections.

1. FARRANTS. The drainage of Brighton. *Sussex Archaeological Collections,* 1986, **124**, 213–214.

19. The Royal Pavilion, and The Dome, Brighton

♣

HEW 501

Royal Pavilion:
TQ 312 042

The Dome,
Brighton:
TQ 312 043

This unique group of buildings forming the Royal Pavilion complex was developed by the Prince of Wales, later King George IV, as a Royal Palace. To suit his exotic taste, the architecture and internal decoration was in an extravagant oriental style. No concessions were made to simplify the hidden structural frames supporting the minarets, domes and pagodas.

In 1787 the Prince Regent acquired a farm house as his residence. This was extended and finally converted into a palace by John Nash between 1815 and 1822. Nash was probably the only architect at the time to build with cast-iron, already in common use by engineers. He had designed several cast-iron bridges[1] and patented their design details. At Brighton he also used laminated timber ribs and prestressed timber beams.

At each end of the pavilion building there is a room 50 ft long by 40 ft wide, stepped in to 32 ft wide, 8 ft from the ends. Both are surmounted by 36 ft high pagodas, stucco clad with timber vertical ribs convex downwards, set on a 42 ft diameter cast-iron ring bearing. This is supported on a square timber frame resting on brick walls on the long side of the room and on cast-iron segmental arch ribs on the shorter sides. The arch ribs are 32 ft span, 8 ft rise, 24 in. wide and 6 in. deep and channel shaped in section. They rest on cast-iron columns in the walls. At the corners of the timber frame the cast-iron ring is supported on 16 ft span squinch beams of four 12 in. by 12 in. timbers with a longitudinal cast-iron insert at the centre intended to act as a flat arch.

Over a central circular reception room of 33 ft diameter, there is an onion dome with a 36 ft maximum diameter, of 32 upright laminated timber ribs supported on a circular cast-iron frame 9 ft deep, with a 30 ft diameter top ring

Dome, Brighton Pavilion

and 35 ft base ring, in turn supported on 16 cast-iron columns built into the walls. Above the frame, six cast-iron columns, 12 ft 9 in. high, support another ring kerb on which rest six cast-iron half trusses 18 ft high, set radially, supporting the top of the onion dome and its surmounting 16 ft high pinnacle.

Ten large minarets rise 48 ft above the building's flat roof. They have a cast-iron hollow tapering core of 2 ft 6 in. diameter at base, clad with Bath stone rings. Those over corridors are supported on four cast-iron trusses 4 ft deep at 2 ft centres on cast-iron columns in the walls.

The room known as Queen Victoria's bedroom has a heavy ornate plaster ceiling supported by 12 in. square prestressed timber beams 26 ft 7 in. span. The beams are halved vertically and sandwich three cast-iron T members to form a shallow internal truss, the timber being in tension. The iron members are compressed by the drawing down of wedges between them by screwing up nuts on square threads. Prestressed beams of this type, but with hardwood compression members and wedges, were known by the mid-eighteenth century.[2]

The building now called the Dome was a stable block designed in 1803 by William Porden to accommodate 44 horses and grooms.[3] It is surmounted by a 41 ft 6 in. radius 80 ft span nearly hemispherical dome topped by a

15 ft diameter lantern and clad in lead and glass supported on 20 laminated timber half-ribs of three thicknesses of 8 in. by 3 in. timber. When the Dome was converted into a concert hall in 1935, it was given a false ceiling.

1. RUDDOCK E. R. *Arch bridges and their builders, 1759-96.* Cambridge University Press, 1979, 140.

2. PRICE F. (Clerk of Works, Salisbury Cathedral). *A treatise on carpentry.* 4th ed. C. Ackers, 1759, 6, plate B.

3. FARRANT S. Physical development of the Royal Pavilion Estate. *Sussex Archaeological Collections,* 1982, **120**, 178.

◆

(demolished)

HEW 428

TQ 315 037

20. Brighton Chain Pier

The construction of a 1134 ft long pier on an open coast line in 1822–23 was a remarkable achievement. Originally it was intended as berthing for a steamer service to France and for coastal shipping but it rapidly became a pleasure attraction for holiday makers.[1]

Captain Samuel Brown was the designer and constructor, his choice of suspension spans being almost inevitable as he was proprietor of a chain works which specialised in suspension bridge chains. In 1820 he built Union Bridge (HEW 143)[2] on the River Tweed using his patent wrought iron chain links.

The pier had four 255 ft spans. Four pairs of cast-iron towers, 25 ft high, supported the chains and were founded on groups of twenty piles. There were four suspension chains on each side, carrying 1 in. diameter wrought iron vertical suspension rods at 5 ft centres to support the deck. The shore anchorage for the suspension chains was in the cliff face; at the seaward end it was provided by a mass of stones. The approach was 13 ft wide, opening out to a 210 ft wide head, 80 ft long. At the towers the approach narrowed to 9 ft.

In 1896 the pier was destroyed by a storm, but it has been immortalised by the seascape paintings of Turner and Constable.

1. BISHOP J. P. *The Brighton chain pier: in memorium.* Brighton, 1897.

2. BARBEY M. F. *Civil engineering heritage: northern England.* Thomas Telford, London, 1981, 14.

21. West Pier and Palace Pier, Brighton

♣

West Pier was the second at Brighton. It was followed by Palace Pier, built near the site of the Chain Pier (HEW 425).

West Pier:
HEW 212
TQ 303 041

A major development in the successful construction of pleasure piers was the use of the screw pile innovated and patented by the blind Irish engineer Alexander Mitchell.[1] It was a cast-iron column usually of 10 in. diameter, with screw shaped wings at the toe, so that it would penetrate the ground by rotation. It could be used on any foreshore from compact sand which would resist percussion driving of solid piles, to soft mud which would not have enough friction to support plain columns but could support the wings of screw piles.

Palace Pier:
HEW 429
TQ 314 038

The first use of these piles for a seaside pier in England was by Eugenius Birch at Margate in 1856.[2] He then used the method at Deal, Brighton West, Eastbourne, Hastings, Bournemouth, Plymouth and eight more sites. Other pier designers followed his example.

Brighton West Pier, opened in 1866, is regarded as Birch's best. It is 1115 ft long and 310 ft wide at the head, having been extended in 1893. The details of the cast and

Palace Pier, Brighton

wrought iron work in column tops, brackets and railings is most elegant. Construction followed well tried practice. Groups of screw piles, braced diagonally with wrought iron tie rods, support cross heads which in turn support open lattice longitudinal girders, with cross beams to support deck plankings. It was built by R. Laidlaw and Son.

Brighton Palace Pier, designed by R. St George Moore, who was involved with the Nab Tower (HEW 1313, p.163), was opened in 1899. It follows the same general method of construction, including screw piles. The length is 1760 ft and the head width 189 ft. It was built by R. Mayoh. The entertainment pavilions on the pier externally echo the oriental architecture of Nash's design for the Royal Pavilion (HEW 501).

These two piers enhance the Brighton sea front which would be monotonous without them. West Pier was the only one Listed Grade I, doubtless because of the fine detailing of the cast-iron work; but it was in poor condition and closed in 1975. Over recent years its condition has further deteriorated and it has suffered extensive storm damage.

1. MITCHELL A. On submarine foundations, particularly the screw pile and moorings. *Min. Proc. Instn Civ. Engrs*, 1848, 7, 108-146.

2. ADAMSON S. H. *Seaside piers*. Batsford, London, 1983, 100-102.

♣ 22. Brighton Marina

HEW 633

TQ 334 032 to
345 031

Brighton Marina was the second artificial harbour built in Britain during the twentieth century, after Dover (HEW 125, p.247). Its forbidding position on an exposed coast, with tall cliffs and narrow beach, was dictated by the requirement that it should be near the Brighton conurbation and with easy access to London.

The Marina[1] is dredged to 12 ft below low water of spring tides, and was expensive to construct, as it is sited on a shallow wave-cut chalk platform. The layout was governed by the need to maintain calm water in the mooring area, to minimize wave action in the outer harbour and to suppress choppy seas caused by wave reflection in the single entrance. These factors were investigated by model study, which determined the po-

Brighton Marina

sition and orientation of the entrance and led to the construction of two wave spending beaches to prevent reflection and two wave screens.

There are two main breakwaters totalling 5000 ft enclosing 150 acres of water and reclaimed land. They are made up of 110 precast concrete circular units, of 41 ft diameter, 28 ft to 41 ft high, founded on the wave-cut platform and joined by tremied concrete and bagwork. They are partially sand filled. The wave spending beaches are on a slope of 1 in 3, armoured with 6 ton patent precast concrete Akmon interlocking units.

The design was by Lewis and Duvivier, consulting engineers, and the contractors were Taylor Woodrow. Work took eight years and was completed in 1979.

There is berthing for 900 yachts in the inner non-tidal basin which is reached via a lock with triple delta gates and spanned by a bascule bridge. The breakwaters received the Concrete Society Award for 1979 in the civil engineering category, and the marina was formally opened by H.M. Queen Elizabeth II in June of that year.

1. TERRETT F. L. et al. Brighton Marina. *Proc. Instn Civ. Engrs*, 1979, Part 1, **66**, 191–208.

◆

HEW 1412

TQ 220 049 to
268 045

23. Shoreham Harbour

A port has been established at the mouth of the river Adur since Roman times. For 300 years, from the Norman period, Shoreham was the largest port on the south coast with ship-building an important industry. During the First World War, numerous concrete barges were built and the Nab Tower (HEW 1313, p.163) was constructed between 1917 and 1919. For much of the twentieth century coal for Brighton's power stations and for gas production has been Shoreham's major import, but this has declined and in the mid-1980s aggregates, oil and timber were the most important commodities.

As at Newhaven (HEW 1414), littoral drift tended to move the river mouth eastwards and marsh reclamation in the Adur Valley contributed to the entrance being kept shallow. Eighteenth century attempts to stabilise the entrance proved unsuccessful and it was not until 1817–21 that the present entrance was established.

An opening was made in the shingle bank at its 1760 site which was 7000 ft to the west of the river mouth. Two 320 ft long timber framed chalk filled training walls formed a 250 ft wide entrance. The river outlet was filled in, thus forming a lagoon behind the shingle beach, which was provided with sluices in the eastern side of the new entrance. Water so retained was discharged at low tide and cleared accreted material from the river. William Chapman,[1] later Engineer of Seaham Harbour, (HEW 758)[2] designed the works and Harbour Master William Clegram acted as Resident Engineer.

In 1826, on Thomas Telford's recommendation, a triangular training pier was built from opposite the centre of the harbour entrance with its point facing seawards. This deflected tidal flows and inhibited the deposition of sediment. A lighthouse was built behind the training pier in 1848 to act as a leading mark. It is now a Grade II Listed Building. The eastern lagoon became known as 'the canal' and its sluices were replaced by a lock, in 1854, which converted it into an elongated, non-tidal basin. The lock was superseded in 1934, when it became a dry dock.

A further major improvement to the harbour entrance was undertaken in 1953[3] when two new breakwaters, 1086 ft long to the west and 800 ft long to the east, moved

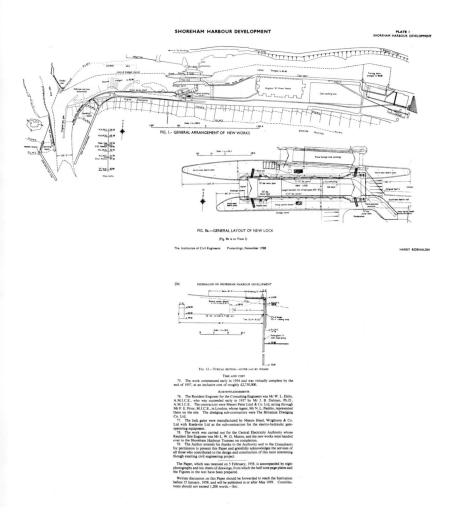

The Institution of Civil Engineers. Proceedings, November 1958

HARRY RIDEHALGH

296   RIDEHALGH ON SHOREHAM HARBOUR DEVELOPMENT

FIG. 13.—TYPICAL SECTION—OUTER LAY-BY WHARF

TIME AND COST

73. The work commenced early in 1957 and was virtually complete by the end of 1957, at an inclusive cost of roughly £2,750,000.

ACKNOWLEDGEMENTS

76. The Resident Engineer for the Consulting Engineers was Mr W. L. Elsby, A.M.I.C.E., who was succeeded early in 1957 by Mr J. B. Dalman, Ph.D., A.M.I.C.E. The contractors were Messrs Peter Lind & Co. Ltd, acting through Mr F. E. Prior, M.I.C.E., in London, whose Agent, Mr N. L. Pashby, represented them on the site. The dredging sub-contractors were The Britannia Dredging Co. Ltd.
77. The lock gates were manufactured by Messrs Head, Wrightson & Co. Ltd with Keelavite Ltd as the sub-contractors for the electro-hydraulic gate-operating equipment.
78. The work was carried out for the Central Electricity Authority whose Resident Site Engineer was Mr L. W. G. Mason, and the new works were handed over to the Shoreham Harbour Trustees on completion.
79. The Author extends his thanks to the Authority and to the Consultants for permission to present this Paper and gratefully acknowledges the services of all those who contributed to the design and construction of this most interesting though exacting civil engineering project.

The Paper, which was received on 5 February, 1958, is accompanied by eight photographs and ten sheets of drawings, from which the half-tone page plates and the Figures in the text have been prepared.

Written discussion on this Paper should be forwarded to reach the Institution before 15 January, 1959, and will be published in or after May 1959. Contributions should not exceed 1,200 words.—Sec.

the harbour entrance 500 ft seawards. A larger lock was provided to enable 4500 ton colliers to deliver to Brighton B power station and additional steel sheet pile wharfs were constructed.

Shoreham Harbour development

1. SKEMPTON A. W. William Chapman (1749-1832), Civil Engineer. *Trans Newcomen Soc.*, 1973–74, 46, 46–82.

2. BARBEY M. F. *Civil engineering heritage: northern England.* Thomas Telford, London, 1981, 18–19.

3. RIDEHALGH H. Shoreham harbour development *Proc. Instn Civ. Engrs*, 1958, **11**, 285–296.

♣ 24. Old Shoreham Trestle Bridge

HEW 468

TQ 206 059

Timber bridges are relatively rare, but there is a good example of the trestle type at Old Shoreham, making an attractive scene with the nearby Norman church. It was originally built in 1781–82 to the design of engineer Joseph Hodskinson for a group headed by the Duke of Norfolk, who wanted to bridge the River Adur for the south coast road.[1]

One hundred and forty six timber piles, in 26 trestles, support the 12 ft wide roadway. Two passing places, 25 ft wide, are included in the 450 ft length of timber work. The approaches are causeways supported by masonry retaining walls.

When the Shoreham to Horsham branch of the London Brighton and South Coast Railway (HEW 1573) was opened in 1861, a level crossing became necessary adjacent to the bridge, so the railway company acquired it and continued with toll charges. In 1916 they replaced the bridge with an almost identical structure, still in timber. In 1968, a new bridge was built for the A27 south coast trunk road. The British Railways Board then ceased to charge tolls and handed the bridge over to the County Council, who maintain it as a footpath.

Shoreham Trestle Bridge

1. SUSSEX ARCHAEOLOGICAL COLLECTIONS. *Notes and Queries*, 1944–45, **10**, 167.

25. Timberley Viaduct

♦

When, in 1861–63, the London Brighton and South Coast Railway (HEW 1573) extended their West Sussex line south from Pulborough to join the Brighton to Portsmouth coastline south of Arundel, the route followed the River Arun gap in the South Downs. Four bridges and four viaducts were required in the valley, the largest of which is Timberley Viaduct with 15 spans and a length of 528 ft., constructed of cast and wrought iron.

HEW 1201

TQ 023 138

The river span is a through structure of wrought iron which has two bowstring girders with unusual end castings that also act as bearers for the adjacent approach spans. The main girders are 106 ft long and set at a skew of 24°. It has apparently been unneccesary to strengthen them because the span was originally designed to carry four tank engines on each track.

The two approach spans adjacent to the main spans are plate girders with top flanges curved in section, a design favoured by I. K. Brunel. They resemble exactly the original wrought iron design, but are said to have been renewed in 1894. Their maximum span is 38 ft and they correct the main span's skew so that the remainder of the approach spans could be built to the standard square design of the nearby smaller viaducts. These have 29 ft spans. Cast-iron girders rest on trestles with cast-iron columns 11 ft long on brick piers. The outer cast-iron beams supporting parapet railings remain but the inner

Timberley Viaduct

four beams supporting the tracks have been replaced by plate girders. The Chief Engineer of the LBSCR at the time was F. D. Banister.

♣

26. Stopham Ancient Bridge

HEW 511

TQ 029 183

Sussex is not well endowed with fine old bridges. The rivers are small and some bridges may have been destroyed by the passage of heavy products from the Wealden iron industry. Jervoise regards Stopham as the best known. It is a Scheduled Ancient Monument.

The original bridge was timber,[1] the masonry structure having probably been built in Elizabethan times. It carries the Pulborough to Petworth road, A283, over the River Arun just at its tidal limit. There are six semicircular arches of 11 ft 9 in. span and a central 12 ft 9 in. span. In 1822 this arch was raised 5 ft, to allow passage of high laden barges on the Arun navigation proceeding to the Wey Arun Junction Canal, opened in 1816. It could be claimed that this spoiled the proportions of the bridge. The stone is local, from the Bargate beds.

In 1865, the bridge was extended at both ends, making an overall length of 246 ft and an extra arch was added for flood relief at the west end, which is on a curve. The

Stopham Ancient Bridge

bridge is 12 ft wide, with nine refuges over the piers. For some years there was single line traffic controlled by traffic lights but damage to the parapet on the inside of the curve became increasingly frequent until a new bridge 100 ft to the north was opened to relieve it of all traffic in 1986.

1. JERVOISE E. *The ancient bridges of the south of England.* Architectural Press, London, 1930, 57.

27. Petworth Dam

HEW 1691

SU 972 218

The lake at Petworth is formed by an earth dam 500 ft in length with a crest 70 ft wide, which carries an estate road, and has a maximum height of 22 ft. Built in 1755–56, it is an early work by Lancelot (Capability) Brown, the celebrated landscape gardener.[1] Beneath pitching and rubble protection on the inner face is a sloping core of clay which extends over part, possibly all, of the lake sides and bottom. The main bank consists of random earth fill. Beneath the bank is a brick outlet culvert controlled by a wooden sluice gate operated from the crest through a vertical shaft. The shaft and culvert are probably surrounded by clay to prevent leakage. The exceptional crest width and flat outer slope, about 1 in 5, suggest that a very considerable volume of earth was excavated to enlarge the lake and used as fill rather than being taken away as spoil.

1. HINDE T. *Capability Brown.* Hutchinson, London, 1986, 49–52.

28. Petworth Ancient Water Supply and Coultershaw Beam Pump

HEW 1436

SU 972 194

Petworth had the benefit of a public water[1] supply as early as 1429, when the rector, Rev. John Edmunds installed a conduit from springs at the junction of the lower greensand and Atherfield clay, 1 mile west of the town. By 1780 the supply was inadequate, so the 3rd Earl Egremont, of Petworth House, decided to pump from the River Rother, 1½ miles to the south. Because the Rother runs in the greensand, he kept the two supplies separate and warned the townsfolk not to drink the river water, as it contained suspended fine sediment. It seems likely that, during earlier visits to London, Lord Egremont had examined the water-wheel driven pumps installed under London Bridge by George Sorocold in 1705 to supply nearby parts of the City. The pump constructed at Coultershaw Bridge in 1784 bore a striking resemblance to a part of that installation.

It is a three-throw beam pump, driven by a water-wheel, originally undershot. The pump stroke is 12½ in. and its plungers are of 6 in. diameter. It pumped against a head of 150 ft delivering water through a 32 in. cast-iron pipe to reservoirs in Petworth Park and in the town. From these reservoirs water was distributed to stand pipes.

Lord Egremont's warning eventually went unheeded, so there was alarm when in 1874, Dr Charles Kelly reported evidence of sewage effluent in the river. Lord Leconfield, of Petworth House, briefed consulting engineers Hassard and Tyrrell, who installed a new supply from shallow bore holes in the lower greensand. This would have been impossible without steam pumping. A 6 h.p. Mason and Weyman steam engine with a Cornish boiler started work in 1883.

The Coultershaw beam pump continued working, however, but only to supply water to Petworth estate for horticulture. It finally stopped in the mid-1950s. The Sussex Industrial Archaeology Society have now restored the pump and it is run for public demonstrations. Because no other beam pump of similar size and age and in working order is known to exist, the Coultershaw pump has been Scheduled as an Ancient Monument.

1. TAYLOR J. E. et al. Petworth water supply. *Sussex Industrial History*, 1980, **10**, 15–22.

29. Stane Street

HEW 1294

TQ 328 803 to SU 864 047

Stane street is a good example of Roman skill in route planning.[1] The road leaves London aimed at Chichester, but deviates southwards to leave the London clay for the chalk. It then runs parallel to the original alignment. A second deviation to the south takes the road down the North Downs scarp across the River Mole and east of Leith Hill. Then a slight westwards reorientation near

Holmwood gives a straight line to Pulborough. Ten miles of this length is now a continuous stretch of the A29 road to Bognor Regis.

In this stretch the River Arun is crossed 1 mile north of Slinfold at TQ 118 331, where wood piles, found in 1934 and dated to Roman times, show that there was a timber bridge.[2] At Pulborough the Arun was recrossed, probably by a ferry, with a 630 yd stone causeway across the marshes.

From the southern river crossing a slight realignment westwards gives a straight line to Chichester allowing a reasonable gradient up the scarp of the South Downs and then a long easy gradient across the dip slope. The first 3 miles from the scarp is National Trust property and may be walked. The agger is prominent, being about 50 ft wide and up to 4 ft high. The easiest access is at the west end (SU 940 105).

A mile from Chichester a section revealed by gravel working showed a formation width of 30 ft wide with a sand on gravel wearing surface and ditches 45 ft apart, on either side.[3]

Chichester, then called Noviomagus, was an administrative and military centre with a port and a mint. Thus good communications with London were needed and this 58 mile long road was constructed, in about 70 A.D.[4] The road also served to distribute grain from Sussex farmlands.

1. WIMBOLT S. E. *Britain under the Romans.* Penguin Books, Harmondsworth, 1945, 13.

2. MARGARY I. D. *Roman ways in the Weald.* Phoenix House, London, 1948, 64.

3. LOWTHER A. W. A section of Stane Street near Chichester. *Sussex Archaeological Collections*, 1942, **82**, 110–112.

4. WIMBOLT S. E. Op cit. 57

30. Cliff Stabilisation, East of Brighton

From Black Rock, Brighton, eastwards to Newhaven there are high chalk cliffs. The Brighton to Newhaven road, A259, runs for 5 miles along the cliff top to Peacehaven and then diverges inland. A residential area began

HEW 1571

TQ 335 033 to
425 003

to develop at Peacehaven after the First World War to house returning servicemen, hence the name. It has continued to expand, many of the side roads and houses being on the seaward side of the main road.

The cliffs are about 100 ft high and exposed to weathering and the foreshore is subject to erosion. In 1867 work started between Brighton and Roedean (TQ 345 031) to stop foreshore erosion by littoral drift. At the time it was estimated that the cliffs had receded 30 ft in the previous 11 years. Mass concrete groynes 250 ft to 450 ft long were constructed about 700 ft apart.

Works to stop erosion between Roedean and Rottingdean (TQ 370 020) started in 1907, when an attempt was made to retain the beach by construction of adjustable height groynes in reinforced concrete. They were constructed to Mouchel-Hennebique design by Holloway Bros.[1] This is claimed to be the first use of reinforced concrete groynes.

In about 1930 cliff stabilisation was started at Black Rock (TQ 335 033) and proceeded eastwards intermittently at points of worst erosion. A mass concrete sea-wall with a promenade was constructed and the chalk face was raked back to a stable angle.

By 1970 the sea-wall was practically continuous to the west end of Peacehaven (TQ 395 013), a distance of around 3½ miles. In 1974-75 surveys revealed that an extension of the work to protect Peacehaven housing over a length of nearly 3 miles had become urgent. It was tackled according to urgency in eight sections.

Careful judgement was needed to decide on cliff slopes and margins from road works to the cliff edge. Where the cliff was sound, the slope adopted was the self-weathering angle of 70 to 80°, with road margins a minimum of 5 ft from the cliff edge, which was fenced. The dip of the chalk varied little from zero, but the plane of some faults sloped obliquely to the foreshore making them difficult to locate. All sections included a reinforced concrete sea-wall and promenade. Mass concrete groynes were also constructed in places. When completed there was a practically continuous sea wall and promenade for some 6 miles. Lewes District Council engineer, R. L. Stammers, was responsible for design and supervision of construction.[2]

1. OWENS J. S. and WOOD F. J. Reinforced concrete sea defences. *Min. Proc. Instn Civ. Engrs*, 1911–12, **189**, 292–307.

2. STAMMERS R. L. Coast defence engineering in East Sussex. *Mun. Engr*, 1982, **109**, 278–286 and 353–359.

31. Lower Ouse Navigation and Newhaven Harbour

The River Ouse is tidal to a point 3 miles above Lewes, which is partially below high water level. The river drains two flat low lying areas — the Brooks, of about 2000 acres is to the south of Lewes and the Laughton Levels, of some 3000 acres is to the east of the town. The mouth of the Ouse was stabilised in its present position in the 1730s and both before and after this time, numerous attempts were made to increase the river's discharge and hence improve drainage of the levels and provide better ship access. From the time of Henry V the river had been banked and in the sixteenth century a new cut was made close to Castle Hill in an attempt to straighten the river's flow into the sea. Around 1770 John Smeaton submitted proposals to straighten the river's course but only Piddinghoe meander was eliminated by a 500 yd cut with minor widening work done elsewhere.[1] Nearly 20 years later, William Jessop[2] recommended a comprehensive schedule of work including a 1000 cut at Southease, a 400 yd cut at Southerham and shoal removal to enable shipping to reach Lewes on any high tide. An authorising Act was passed in 1791 and work extended over the next ten years, by which time Cater Rand, a well-known local civil engineer appointed as supervisor, was able to claim that 4000 acres of the levels were freed from flooding[3]. Regrettably increased costs resulted in some items of work being abandoned including the removal of shoals.

No port of substance was established at the Ouse's mouth until John Reynolds constructed training piers between 1733–35 and stabilised the entrance around which Newhaven Harbour grew. As with Shoreham (HEW 1412) eastwards littoral drift continued to cause difficulties which were further alleviated in 1843 when

Lower Ouse Navigation:
HEW 1696
TQ 419 102 to
452 000

Newhaven Harbour:
HEW 1414
TQ 466 017 to
452 994

Newhaven
Harbour

the Harbour Master, W. Stevens, suggested the construction of a 500 ft long groyne sited 150 ft to the west of the training wall. It was built by James Walker and enabled an entrance depth of 7 ft below low water of spring tides to be maintained. This encouraged the London, Brighton and South Coast Railway (LBSCR)(HEW 1573) to transfer their cross channel service from Shoreham (HEW 1412). Rail access to suitable wharfs was completed in 1847.

Further major development started in 1878[4]. The west training wall and groyne were replaced by a 930 yd curving breakwater, sited 400 yd west of the ship channel. It was constructed of mass concrete on blockwork and had a parapet level 40 ft above low water. The railway wharf was extended by 600 yd in timber piling and the east training wall was also lengthened. F. D. Banister, Chief Engineer to the LBSCR, designed the work. All the main berths have been subsequently faced with steel sheet piling and roll-on, roll-off facilities were provided in the mid-1960s.

Until 1784, the river could only be crossed by ferry. A timber drawbridge was then constructed which was replaced in 1865 by a 150 ft long, wrought iron plate girder swing bridge which carried the A259, Eastbourne to Newhaven road together with rail access to western wharfs. It was replaced in 1976 by an all-welded swing bridge which only carried road access.

1. FARRANT J. H. The evolution of Newhaven Harbour and the Lower Ouse before 1800. *Sussex Archaeological Collections*, 1972, **110**, 44-59.

2. HADFIELD H. and SKEMPTON A. W. *William Jessop Engineer*. David and Charles, Newton Abbot, 1979, 248.

3. FARRANT J. H. Civil engineering in Sussex around 1800 and career of the Cater Rand. *Sussex Industrial History*, 1973-74, **6**, 2–14.

4. CAREY A. E. Harbour improvements at Newhaven, Sussex. *Min. Proc. Instn Civ. Engrs*, 1886, **87**, 92–113.

32. Beachy Head Lighthouse

HEW 77

TV 583 951

Beachy Head Lighthouse is the best known in Sussex and stands 550 ft off-shore, guarding the 600 ft high chalk headland. An earlier lighthouse at Belle Tout, 2200 yd west, stood on a low cliff but it suffered from obliteration by low cloud and in 1896 was threatened by cliff falls.

A new lighthouse, to be sited in the sea directly in front of Beachy Head, was therefore designed in 1897 by Thomas Matthews, Engineer-in-Chief to Trinity House.[1] The shape, part of a vertical ellipse, was orthodox for lighthouses in the sea, following Smeaton's Eddystone Lighthouse (HEW 73, p.48). It was to be founded in the chalk, 9 ft 6 in. below low water on a concrete apron 80 ft diameter, the 112 ft high tower being 47 ft diameter at the base. The masonry is solid up to 10 ft 6 in. above high tide, when it becomes 4 ft 3 in. thick reducing to 2 ft at balcony level.

To obtain access for construction, the Contractors, Bullivant and Company, constructed a temporary platform 37 ft by 26 ft, 23 ft above high water on nine steel piles. This was reached by an aerial ropeway from the top of the cliff. It was sited so that a derrick crane on it could plumb the construction. Work started in September 1899 and was completed in April 1903.

Fine grain Cornish granite was used for the tower, the blocks being dovetailed together horizontally and vertically in courses 1 ft 10 in. deep with 3/16 in. mortar joints. At the lantern level the tower is corbelled out from 18 ft

Beachy Head Lighthouse. Courtesy of Skyfotos Ltd, Kent

diameter to 24 ft diameter for the balcony. The light is a revolving dioptric of 880 000 candle power with its focal plane 103 ft above high water. It was converted to remote control from North Foreland lighthouse (HEW 733, p.245) in 1983.

1. CASE A. H. Construction of Beachy Head Lighthouse. *Min. Proc. Instn Civ. Engrs*, 1904-05, **159**, 267–280.

33. Royal Sovereign Lighthouse ◆

HEW 734

TV 719 944

Some lighthouses built during the twentieth century have been fabricated ashore, towed to site and settled on the seabed, in much the same way as oil rigs are currently handled. Nab Tower (HEW 1313, p.163) built in 1920, Kish Bank, Dublin Bay, in 1965, and Royal Sovereign, in 1971, are examples.

Royal Sovereign was the first lighthouse in the United Kingdom to be provided with a helicopter pad as part of the design; it replaced a lightship on a shoal, 7 miles south-east of Eastbourne, which had been marked by a light since 1875. Its light is 90 ft above sea-level and has a range of 28 miles. The mounting is a 38 ft high steel tower at a corner of the 60 ft square helicopter pad which forms the roof of a reinforced concrete box. The box housed the crew, generators and stores. To support the structure above water level there is a central 14 ft diameter concrete tower, in turn supported on a cellular reinforced concrete box 102 ft square 16 ft 6 in. deep with a central socket for the tower.[1]

Two separate excavations were made in low ground behind a high shingle bank east of Newhaven Port. In one, the base and tower were constructed, in the other the superstructure. Gaps were then dredged for removal. The base was floated out, towed to site and sunk with the main tower retracted into it. A temporary pile structure supported the superstructure during construction, so that it could be picked up on barges during flooding and dropped on the main tower when in position on site, by flooding the barges. The telescopic section of the main tower was then jacked up to full height using twelve 150 ton jacks. The total height of the structure is 159 ft 10 in.,

Royal Sovereign
Lighthouse.
Courtesy of
Skyfotos Ltd, Kent

and it was commissioned in 1971. Design was by Halcrow and Partners and construction by Christani and Nielsen.

1. ANTONAKIS C. J. A problem of designing and building a structure at sea. *Proc. Instn Civ. Engrs*, 1972, **52**, 95–126.

34. Section of Roman Road, Holtye   ◆

In 1929 a Roman road running from north to south in East Sussex was discovered by aerial photography.[1] It forked south from Watling Street in the vicinity of New Cross and passed through West Wickham, Crockham Hill, Edenbridge, Holtye and Camp Hill, intersecting an east–west road along the foot of the South Downs near Ringmer at TR 424 114. It ascended the scarp to divide into tracks to Brighton, Seaford and Eastbourne. It may have been used for moving the products of the Roman Wealden iron industry to the ports and to London.

At Holtye a 100 ft length of the road was uncovered by the Sussex Archaeological Society and left exposed for viewing.[2] This was possible because the surface had been made of iron furnace cinder which has become a hard impervious layer over the centuries due to the rusting of the iron. There are wheel marks on the surface and it is traversed by a small stream. The width varies from 13 ft to 23 ft and the camber from flat to 8 in. Construction thickness is estimated to be up to 12 in. at the centre and 3 in. at the edges. The approach is along a footpath, south from the A264 East Grinstead to Tunbridge Wells road.

HEW 740

TQ 462 387

1. MARGARY I. D. *Roman ways in the Weald.* Phoenix House, London, 1948, 45–92.

2. MARGARY I. D. *Sussex Archaeological Collections*, 1940, **81**, 43–53.

Roman Road

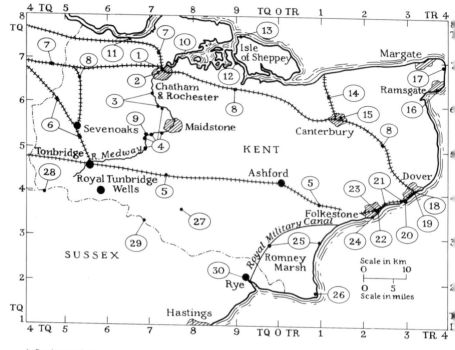

1. Rochester Bridges
2. M2 Medway Bridge
3. Medway Navigation
4. Medway Ancient Bridges
5. The South Eastern Railway
6. Polhill Tunnel and Sevenoaks Tunnel
7. Strood and Higham Tunnels
8. The London, Chatham and Dover Railway
9. Bow Bridge, Wateringbury
10. Chatham Dockyard
11. Gravesend Piers
12. Kingsferry Lift Bridge
13. Sheerness Boat Store
14. The Canterbury and Whitstable Railway
15. Canterbury Cathedral Water Supply
16. Royal Harbour Ramsgate
17. North Foreland Lighthouse
18. Dover Harbour
19. Dover Pharos
20. Channel Tunnel Works
21. Shakespeare and Abbotscliff Tunnels
22. Folkestone Harbour
23. Foord Viaduct, Folkestone
24. Folkestone Cliff Railway
25. Romney Marsh Reclamation
26. Dungeness Lighthouses
27. Union Mill, Cranbrook
28. Cowden Dams
29. Bewl Bridge Reservoir and Dam
30. Rye Ancient Water Supply

8. Kent

Kent has a long and varied coastline. To the north it forms one boundary of the Thames estuary, whereas to the south are the extremely congested shipping lanes of the English Channel. Lighthouses are common coastal features, typified by those at Dungeness and North Foreland; the Roman Pharos in Dover Castle is one of the nation's earliest surviving examples. Romney and adjacent marshes are amongst the country's largest drained and reclaimed areas and illustrate both sea defences and drainage works. There are many harbours, which for centuries have provided cross channel trading links and in times of war have contributed to the nation's defence. Those on the relatively exposed south-east coast, like Folkestone and Dover, have required significant breakwaters for protection and have had to address the siltation problems brought about by the littoral drift. Dock facilities to the north, typified by Gravesend Piers and Chatham Dockyard are sited in relatively sheltered locations but have had to deal with problems associated with their estuarine environment. Some of the buildings in Chatham Dockyard, together with the Boat Store at Sheerness, provide important examples of nineteenth century development in the use of iron in building frames.

The county has been termed 'the garden of England', a title which reflects its agricultural character and suggests the relative absence of major industrial activity. It has not been completely absent, however. Chatham Dockyard was the largest employer of civilian labour in the whole of South-East England for part of the eighteenth century. Coal had been mined since just before the 1914–18 war until the industry's recent demise and in the sixteenth century the Wealden iron industry was well established. Two earth dams at Cowden were built to support iron making activities and the Medway Navigation was constructed partly to convey iron to Maidstone, the Medway's tidal limit. However, as well as serving as a trade route, the Medway has also been one of the principal obstacles on the route from London to Canterbury and hence to the East Kent Channel ports. The Romans' Watling Street crossed the Medway at Durobrivae (Rochester) which has remained the crossing point for the county's major east–west transport route, with road, rail and motorway bridges closely aligned. Further up the Medway and on its tributaries are many examples of medieval masonry bridges like that at Aylesford, constructed initially to serve local community needs.

The relatively short Canterbury and Whitstable Railway was the nation's first passenger and freight line but Kent's railway history has been marked by the nineteenth century rivalry between the South Eastern and the London Chatham and Dover Companies. Neither proved able to dominate the prestigious London to Dover route and a working union was agreed in 1899. Kent's topography required the construction of numerous tunnels, like that at Sevenoaks, one of the nation's longest, together with impressive bridges and viaducts, like those at Lullingstone and Folkestone.

Bewl Bridge reservoir and dam, although relatively modern, are good examples of works associated with the water supply industry. Other examples of this important utility are the quaint cistern at Rye and the even older supply to Canterbury Cathedral.

1. Rochester Bridges: Medieval and earlier bridges, Road Bridge 1856 and rebuilding 1914, Railway Bridge 1858 and rebuilding 1970 and Railway Bridge 1891

The first Rochester Bridge[1] is believed to have been built in Roman times to carry Watling Street across the Medway. A Saxon bridge was built in 960, which consisted of knee braced timber beams spanning 43 ft and wooden plank decking giving a width of 10 ft. It was burnt twice and swept away by flood in 1281. Edward III repaired it in 1344 in order to carry his army to Dover but it was later part demolished on threat of French invasion. In 1387 work started on an eleven-span stone arch bridge which took five years to complete and lasted for nearly 500 years. It was built a little upstream of the older bridge and was 566 ft in length and 15 ft wide. Each pier was 45 ft by 20 and was founded on 20 ft elm piles driven into chalk. The work was probably supervised by Henry Yevele, the King's Stone Mason. By the beginning of the nineteenth century the increase in road and river traffic, combined with Admiralty concern regarding shoaling, resulted in John Rennie supervising extensive improvement works around 1820. The bridge was widened, its arches rounded and a new arch replaced the central pair. Elegant stone balustrading was provided.

It became apparent that Rennie's improvements were not sufficient and finally it was decided to build a new arch bridge[2] to the design of William Cubitt. This was of cast iron with three spans of 140 ft, 170 ft and 140 ft between abutments. At the Strood end a 50 ft swing bridge provided passage for masted vessels. The improved bridge was 40 ft wide and provided an 18 ft river clearance at the centre arch.

The line of the bridge between Rochester and Strood High Streets reverted to that of Watling Street. It was planned to found both abutments and piers on 6 ft or 7 ft diameter cast-iron piles which were to be excavated pneumatically[3], as had been done successfully at Liverpool. However, since ground conditions were very dif-

Medieval and earlier bridges: HEW 1605

Road Bridge 1856 and rebuilding 1914: HEW 1604

Railway Bridge 1858 and rebuilding 1970: HEW 1649

Railway Bridge 1891: HEW 1648

TQ 741 689

ferent — gravel and chalk rather than estuarine silt and there was much debris from previous construction works — it proved a complete failure at Rochester. The 70 cast-iron cylinders, some to a depth of 45 ft, were sunk under air pressure by hand excavation which proved hard and exhausting work and took three years to complete. This innovative technique was developed by John D'Urban Hughes.[3] Work on the new bridge commenced in 1850 and it opened in 1856. The main contractors were Cochrane and Company with Fox Henderson and Company sub-contracting for the masonry. A year later the medieval bridge was blown up by the Royal Engineers and its balustrading used to form part of Rochester Esplanade.

Around the same time, William Cubitt's son, Joseph, designed an adjacent wrought iron, plate girder railway bridge for the East Kent Railway Company. Completed in 1858 by contractors Fox Henderson, it provided an opening span and was founded on 6 to 7 ft diameter cast-iron piles similar to the road bridge.

In 1891 railway company rivalry resulted in the South Eastern Railway (SER) completing a steel lattice girder bridge a few yards downstream of the existing railway crossing. It had four spans varying in length from 127 ft to 181 ft 6 in. and its brick and concrete piers were aligned with those of the two upstream bridges. Rationalisation of the railway companies caused all trains to be switched to the SER bridge in 1911 except for a period after 1919 when fire damage to the SER bridge resulted in the older railway bridge being temporarily recommissioned. Repair and strengthening works were completed in 1922 by the Cleveland Bridge Company and the SER bridge has subsequently carried all rail traffic.

By the end of the nineteenth century further improvements to William Cubitt's road bridge became necessary and it was decided to replace the cast-iron arches by hog-backed steel Pratt trusses to the design of John James Robson. The existing foundations were retained, but the piers were pulled down to cutwater level and rebuilt, leaving the cast-iron skew-backs to the arches in position. The bridge is now 46 ft wide between parapets, 30 ft centre to centre of main girders, with a 26 ft wide carriageway and 7 ft wide cantilevered footways. Clearance underneath the bridge was increased by about 6 ft. The work was undertaken by John Cochrane and Son between 1910–14 and the swing bridge at the Strood end was fixed.

Road traffic again began to outstrip the capacity of Rochester Bridge in the 1950s. The problem was addressed by the provision of a second bridge for eastbound traffic using the piers of the adjoining disused East Kent Railway Bridge. The new superstructure consists of twin welded steel continuous box girders with a compositely acting reinforced concrete deck carrying three traffic lanes. There are three spans of 154, 186 and 154 ft respectively with a total bridge length of 656 ft. Designer of the bridge was Kenneth Anderson with main Contractors A. E. Farr Ltd and Cleveland Bridge and Engineering Company. It was opened in April 1970.

The road bridges at Rochester are owned by the Rochester Bridge Trust, an independent body founded in 1398 by Richard II's Letters Patent. Over the centuries it has accumulated estates and investments which have provided the means for the Bridge Wardens to maintain and construct bridges over the Medway without recourse to public funds.

1. *Crossing the Medway. The story of the Rochester Bridge Trust.* Rochester Bridge Trust.

2. HUMBER W. *Cast and wrought iron bridge construction.* Spon, 1861, I 166–168, II Plates 1–15.

3. HUGHES J. Pneumatic method of constructing the foundation of the new bridge across the Medway at Rochester. *Min. Proc. Instn Civ. Engrs,* 1851, 10, 353–369.

2. The M2 Medway Bridge

Completed in 1964 to the design of Freeman Fox and Partners,[1] the M2 Medway Bridge carries the London to East Kent Motorway and is located 1½ miles upstream of the Rochester Bridge (HEW 1604), which conveys the A2 London to Dover Road. The bridge has a 500 ft main river span with two adjoining 312 ft 6 in. river spans meeting the approaches. There are eleven spans in the 1350 ft west approach and seven in the 797 ft eastern approach resulting in an overall length of 3272 ft. The bridge

HEW 32

TQ 720 667 to 730 664

Medway Bridge — width is 113 ft, its river clearance about 100 ft and it is founded in chalk on either heavy precast reinforced concrete piles or spread footings.

The design called for the production and handling of 162 precast, prestressed beams up to 135 ft in length for the approaches. Manufactured on site, they were positioned on the abutments and approach piers with the aid of a purpose-built launching girder. The Medway Conservancy Board required a clear 400 ft river width during construction which led to the adoption of the cantilever building method for the river spans. This involved casting a section of beam, stressing it back to the previously cast section and then using it to support the formwork for the next section. Contractors Christiani and Nielsen used the Macalloy bar system for stressing and working in 10 ft increments from the two river piers, arched out impressively over the main river span until the two cantilevered beams could be joined in the centre by a suspended span.[2] At the time, the beams were the longest in the world to be constructed by the cantilever method.

1. KERENSKY O. A. and LITTLE G. Medway bridge design. *Proc. Instn Civ.Engrs*, 1964, **29**, Oct., 19–52.

2. KIER M. et al., Medway bridge construction. *Proc. Instn Civ. Engrs*, 1964, **29**, Oct., 53–100.

3. Medway Navigation

♠

HEW 1606

TQ 747 581 to
593 464

For many centuries trade from mid-Kent was conveyed by road to Maidstone, the tidal limit of the Medway, and from thence by sea to its destination. The sixteenth and seventeenth centuries saw an increase in commercial activity, particularly in iron and timber from the Weald and this resulted in plans to make the Medway navigable above Maidstone. Parliamentary powers were obtained in 1664 but no effective action was taken until a further Act in 1740. This empowered 'The Company of the Proprietors of the Navigation of the River Medway' to make the river navigable from Maidstone to Forest Row, a distance of about 30 miles.[1] Between 1740 and 1743 the 15½ mile stretch of river from Maidstone to Tonbridge was canalised by the construction of 14 locks, tow paths, bank protection, dredging and other works. The Company opened the river to traffic in 1743 with manually hauled barges of about 40 tons capacity. Later, horse haulage was introduced increasing the speed of towage from 2 to 2½ miles/h. In favourable conditions the passage could take 10 hours. Trade was in iron, timber, corn, hops, wool and leather downstream and coal, lime, stone and imported timber upstream.

In 1792, an Act was passed which allowed improvements to be carried out to the tidal section of the Medway below Maidstone. The Lower Medway Company was formed and constructed a tidal lock at Allington and carried out dredging and other works, including modification to the medieval bridge at Aylesford (HEW 475).

With the arrival of the South Eastern Railway at Tonbridge in 1842, the fortunes of the hitherto prosperous Medway Navigation began to decline and the Company's revenue was so reduced that essential works could not be carried out. Eventually, in 1911, the Navigation was taken over by the Medway Conservancy Board which undertook substantial improvements. The number of locks was reduced to ten; each inland lock provided a fall of about 6 ft and was capable of accommodating a craft 80 ft by 18 ft 6 in. with a carrying capacity of 120 tons. Traffic did not revive on the river and by the 1930s commercial traffic above Maidstone had ceased but remained on the Lower Medway until the 1960s. Following various local government reorganisations the whole of the Medway Navigation between Allington and Tonbridge, a distance of 17½ miles, is owned and operated by the National Rivers Authority and is used almost entirely by pleasure craft.

1. HADFIELD C. *The canals of southern England*. Phoenix, 1955, 101–8.

4. Medway Ancient Bridges: Aylesford, East Farleigh, Teston, Twyford and Yalding Town

♣

Aylesford:
HEW 475
TQ 729 589

East Farleigh:
HEW 128
TQ 735 535

Teston:
HEW 487
TQ 708 533

Twyford:
HEW 557
TQ 691 499

Yalding Town:
HEW 556
TQ 697 500

Aylesford Bridge is the first of a series of five medieval Kentish ragstone bridges[1] encountered when travelling upstream from the mouth of the River Medway, which still carries one-way traffic. When first constructed, it is believed in the fourteenth century, it had a road width of 13 ft and its total length of 300 ft was divided into seven pointed arch spans ranging in length from about 30 ft to 13 ft 6 in. Around 1824 the proprietors of the Medway Navigation (HEW 1606) replaced the two central river arches by a single 60 ft elliptical span; this provided a low tide river clearance of 20 ft 6 in. and eased the passage of river traffic. The adjacent piers were strengthened by the addition of buttresses and cantilevered pedestrian refuges were provided. Similar refuges exist above the

Aylesford Bridge

triangular cutwaters of the northern piers. Further pier strengthening work was carried out in 1938, which involved protective steel sheet piling and concrete underpinning.

A little to the south-west of Maidstone, the East Farleigh Bridge carries traffic between East Farleigh village and Barming. The 11 ft 6 in. wide road is conveyed over a 300 ft length by five pointed arches with a maximum span of 26 ft 6 in. The four main arches have narrow structural ribs which acted as centring during construction. It is believed to have been constructed in the fourteenth or fifteenth centuries. The fifth arch, over a tow path, was probably added by the Navigation Company around the start of the nineteenth century. The bridge's piers have substantial cutwaters but despite its narrow width, no provision is made for pedestrian refuge. Jervoise[2] proposes the structure as 'the finest bridge in the South of England... a perfect example of medieval design and workmanship'.

Teston Bridge crosses the Medway between Teston village and West Farleigh. It dates from at least 1526 when it is recorded that a legacy contributed to its repairs. Originally it comprised three river spans and four flood arches but one of the latter was lost during extensive repairs in 1830. A little earlier in 1793 the centre span was enlarged to improve navigation. The bridge length is 216 ft,

Opposite: East Farleigh Bridge

Yalding Town Bridge

its road width is only 11 ft 6 in. and the largest span is 24 ft 6 in. Pedestrian refuges are provided above the central cutwaters.

Two bridges are associated with the village of Yalding. Twyford Bridge links Yalding with East Peckham. It was mentioned in fifteenth century wills and the earliest record of it is in 1325 concerning responsibility for repairs. Its 300 ft length is conveyed on five arches of maximum span 16 ft 9 in. The pointed arch shapes are rather unusual in that their lower radii are relatively large. The roadway is 12 ft wide and the substantial cutwaters provide pedestrian recesses. The brickwork parapet is a later addition. Yalding Town Bridge conveys traffic over the River Beult, the Medway's largest tributary. Its length of 455 ft is carried on three river and three flood arches of 25 ft maximum span. The bridge was mentioned in fifteenth century wills and underwent significant alteration in 1848 when its width was increased generally from about 10 ft, to comprise a 10 ft 6 in. roadway and a 3 ft footpath, and locally to 21 ft to provide a passing place.

All five foregoing bridges are Scheduled Ancient Monuments.

1. *British bridges*. Public Works, Road and Transport Congress, London, 1933, 140 (Aylesford), 142 (East Farleigh), 143 (Teston), 146 (Twyford), 147 (Yalding).

2. JERVOISE E. *The ancient bridges of the South of England*. Architectural Press, London 1930, 36.

5. The South Eastern Railway

♠

HEW 1448

TQ 330 800 to
TR 320 405

The first two railways in Kent were the local lines of the Canterbury and Whitstable, 1830 (HEW 476), and the London and Greenwich (LGR), 1836 (HEW 1725, TQ 330 800 to 392 779). Various schemes from the capital to Dover were proposed and in 1836 the South Eastern Railway Act was passed authorising a railway from London Bridge to Dover via Croydon, Tonbridge, Ashford and Folkestone. As described under The London and Brighton Railway (HEW 1573, p.183) construction commenced from Redhill under the supervision of William Cubitt working to plans initially produced by Henry Palmer.

The 46 miles between Redhill and Ashford over the Wealden clay are straight and apart from the 1324 yd Bletchingley Tunnel (HEW 1531 p.185), presented few constructional problems. The line continues to rise after Ashford at 1 in 250–280 for 8 miles to a summit and then descends at 1 in 266 for twelve miles to sea-level at Dover. This last stretch of line required some major works; two short tunnels, an imposing brick viaduct at Folkestone (HEW 482), the 1933 yd Abbotscliff Tunnel (HEW 1393) and the 1392 yd twin bore Shakespeare Cliff Tunnel (HEW 483). In addition, the line had to traverse 2 miles of unstable undercliff at the Warren (HEW 1669), where the gault clay outcrops the chalk. Between Abbotscliff and Shakespeare Tunnels a spectacular blasting operation, involving 8 tons of gunpowder, was required to remove a promontory of unstable chalk. A timber viaduct carried the railway to a harbour terminus at Dover. The 88 mile line from London to Dover was opened on 7 February 1844[1] with a journey time of three hours for fast trains.

Cubitt was an early exponent of the transverse sleeper road[2]. The track was laid on 8 ft long triangular fir sleepers placed apex down. The rails were double headed, weighed 71 lb/yd and were held by ash wedges into cast-iron chairs which were oak trenailed to the planed top surface of the sleeper. Platform loops were provided at some of the principal stations.

Difficulties of operation and competition with the LGR, which owned London Bridge Station and its approaches, led the South Eastern Railway (SER), in conjunction with the London and Croydon Railway, to build a new station, Bricklayers Arms,[3,4] which opened in 1844. The junction with the LGR route to London Bridge was the first to be provided with interlocking signals. The effective operational life of Bricklayers Arms was short because, in 1845, the SER leased the operation of the LGR and passenger services increasingly returned to the more conveniently sited London Bridge Station. However, the SER wished to have a West End and a City terminus and, after absorbing the Charing Cross Railway Company, built stations at Charing Cross and Cannon Street, which opened respectively in 1864 and 1866.

Competition with the London, Chatham and Dover Railway (LCDR) (HEW 1760) which had a terminus at Victoria, resulted in the SER deciding to construct a cut-off line from New Cross to Tonbridge, avoiding Redhill and shortening the distance to Dover by thirteen miles. This 24 mile line entailed major engineering works. Commencing at New Cross the line climbs for 11 miles at 1 in 120–140, the last 3 miles of which are in a deep chalk cutting. It then descends through the 1 mile 849 yd wet Polhill Tunnel (HEW 1610), the l mile 1691 yd Sevenoaks Tunnel (HEW 1394) and finishes with a 6 mile descent at 1 in 122 with a sharp curve to Tonbridge. The line was completed for traffic in 1868.

Several attempts were made over the years for an amalgamation between the SER and the LCDR and finally, in 1899, a working union was authorised by Parliament and came to be known as the South Eastern and Chatham Railway.

1. KIDNER R. W. *The South Eastern Railway and the SE&CR*. The Oakwood Press, Godstone, 1953, 7.

2. POPE J. Description of the permanent way of the South-Eastern Railway. *Min. Proc. Instn Civ. Engrs*, 1842–43, **2**, 72–80.

3. JACKSON A. A. *London's termini*. David and Charles, Newton Abbot, 1969, 147–150.

4. COURSE E. *London's railways*. Batsford, London, 1962, 69–73.

6. Polhill Tunnel and Sevenoaks Tunnel

◆

The Polhill and Sevenoaks tunnels[1] were constructed between 1864 and 1868 and were designed by Peter Ashcroft, Engineer to the South Eastern Railway (HEW 1448). The Polhill Tunnel, 1 mile 849 yd in length, commences in a deep chalk cutting and passes under the summit of the North Downs. Built through sound chalk, only its roof required lining with a semicircular brick arch, 18 in. thick with a 28 ft 8 in. diameter at the springing. In places water seepage has disintegrated the arch's chalk supports and brickwork repairs have been completed. Five working shafts were sunk during the construction varying in depth between 188 ft and 219 ft and some 190 000 yd^3 of chalk were excavated. The tunnel is 22 ft high, carries two tracks and falls at a gradient of 1 in 43 towards Sevenoaks.

With a length of 1 mile 1691 yd, Sevenoaks is the longest mainline tunnel in the South of England. It was constructed in clay and greensand and its horse-shoe section was completely lined with brickwork varying in thickness from 1 ft 10½ in. to 3 ft 0 in., with an 18 in. thick invert. Fifteen working shafts of depths between 116 ft and 394 ft were sunk and some 276 000 yd^3 of material were excavated. It is 24 ft 8 in. wide and 25 ft high from

Polhill Tunnel:
HEW 1610
TQ 494 623 to
506 603

Sevenoaks Tunnel:
HEW 1394
TQ 526 544 to
535 515

Sevenoaks Tunnel

soffit to invert, the twin rail tracks are about 4 ft 6 in. above invert and its gradient falls at 1 in 144 towards Tonbridge.

1. BLOWER A. *British railway tunnels*. Ian Allan, London, 1964, 32 (Sevenoaks), 45–46 (Polhill).

7. The Strood and Higham Railway Tunnels

♦

HEW 486

TQ 717 724 to 740 697

The Strood and Higham tunnels[1,2] were originally constructed as a single waterway tunnel by the Gravesend and Medway Canal Company. Designed by William Tierney Clark and built in the early 1820s, it carried the canal for nearly 4000 yd through the chalk ridge at Higham. It is possible that Clark made the first use of a transit instrument to set out the tunnel line over the undulating ground[3]. When completed, it was the country's second longest tunnel but had the largest cross section, being elliptically shaped, 35 ft high and about 26 ft 6 in. wide. In 1830 it was decided to provide a passing place for vessels, which was achieved by excavating down to the tunnel from a relatively low spot above. Thus the tunnel was divided into the Strood and Higham sections of lengths 2329 yd and 1531 yd respectively.

The canal did not prove a commercial success and in 1845 a single rail track for the South Eastern Railway (SER) (HEW 1448) was constructed partly on the towpath and partly on timber decking over the water. Later in the year the SER bought out the Canal Company, the waterway was filled in and a second track forming part of the North Kent line was laid.

Driven through chalk, about half of the total length is brick lined, a small section of the roof is supported by steel sheets on steel portal frames and the remainder is unlined.

1. HADFIELD C. *The canals of south and south east England*. David and Charles, Newton Abbot, 1969, 60–80.

2. BLOWER A. *British railway tunnels*. Ian Allan, London, 1964, 50–51.

3. SIMMS F. W. *The public works of Great Britain*. Weale, London, 1838, 242–4.

8. The London, Chatham and Dover Railway and Lullingstone Viaduct

Parliamentary approval for the East Kent Railway was obtained in 1853. Commencing at Strood, the North Kent branch terminus of the South Eastern Railway (SER) (HEW 1448), it bridged the Medway to Rochester (HEW 1648) and proceeded to Faversham via Chatham and Sittingbourne. The line was opened in 1858 and was followed by an extension to Canterbury, in 1860. After Canterbury, the line climbed onto the Kent Downs and through the 1 mile 609 yd Lydden Tunnel[1] which has a segmented arch profile of height 21 ft and width 24 ft. From the tunnel the line descended the 7 miles to Dover and was completed in 1861. By this time, the renamed London, Chatham and Dover Railway (LCDR)[2] had been able to reach Victoria Station via a western extension from Strood to St Mary Cray. This extension is heavily graded and commences with a reverse curve from Strood's Medway bridge followed by a 5 mile climb at 1 in 100 up the side of the Medway Valley to Sole Street Station. Six years later, a line via Herne Hill shortened this route and a new city terminus at Holborn Viaduct was completed. In 1863, a major branch line was completed from Faversham to Herne Bay, Margate and

The London, Chatham and Dover Railway: HEW 1760 TQ 290 805 to TR 317 405

Lullingstone Viaduct: HEW 538 TQ 534 657

Lullingstone Viaduct

233

Ramsgate Harbour (HEW 484). Throughout the LCDR's life, competition with the SER was intense and eventually a working union was agreed in 1899.

The most impressive structure in the LCDR's network is the Lullingstone, or Eynsford Viaduct[3] crossing the Darenth Valley on a branch line between Swanley Junction and Sevenoaks. It was completed in June 1862 for the Sevenoaks Railway Company[4] which was subsequently taken over by the LCDR. The designer was F. T. Turner and it comprised nine, five ring semicircular arches of 30 ft span supported on slender tapering brick piers with a maximum height from ground to soffit of 63 ft. The top of the red brickwork had two string courses, one moulded, separated by block dentillation with a contrasting open stone parapet above.

1. BLOWER A. *British railway tunnels*, Ian Allan, London, 1964, 49.

2. KIDNER R. W. *The London, Chatham and Dover Railway*. The Oakwood Press, Godstone, 1952.

3. BIDDLE G. and NOCK O. S. *The railway heritage of Britain*. Joseph, London, 1983, 186.

4. CARTER E. F. *An historical geography of the railways of the British Isles*. Cassell, London, 1959, 300.

♣

9. Bow Bridge, Wateringbury

HEW 1392

TQ 691 528

Bow Bridge, which replaced an earlier timber structure, was completed in 1915 by the Yorkshire Hennebique Company of Leeds. It carries a minor road over the River Medway between Wateringbury and Yalding. The five flood and four river spans, each of 28 ft 6 in. are supported on two leg trestles which are founded on concrete piles driven into clay. The river clearance is about 11 ft, the width between the parapets is 18 ft and originally the middle spans had concrete balustrading cantilevered from the main beams, which was replaced by steel panels in 1981. Although the reinforced main beams have soffits which curve down to the tops of the trestle heads, they are straight for most of their length and contrast with the curved arch ribs used on the Tuckton Bridge, Dorset (HEW 993 p.125) completed ten years earlier. Both were designed by L. G. Mouchel using Hennebique reinforced concrete. Thus Bow Bridge illustrates a significant devel-

opment in the use of reinforced concrete in bridge building. A 4 ton load limit was imposed in 1968.

Bow Bridge

10. Chatham Dockyard: covered slipways and Iron framed workshops

♦

Between 1836 and 1855, a group of five large covered
slipways, Nos 3 to 7, were built at the northern end of
Chatham Dockyard[1]. It had become the practice to provide roofs over ship building slips to lessen the occur-
rence of rot in the timbers. Of the slips, only No.7 remains,
having been used until 1966 for its original purpose. The
roofs are some of the nation's earliest long-span timber
and iron structures[2].

In 1838, No.3 was the first slip constructed and this had
a timber roof of the type developed by Sir Robert Sep-
pings, Surveyor to the Navy Board. It is some 300 ft long,
with an overall width of 146 ft and a clear span of 93 ft
over the slip. The roof's shore end is closed by a curved
section. Massive pitch pine trusses support the boarded
and asbestos sheeted roof, with the whole structure carried on 52 timber stancions socketed into cast-iron feet.
A wooden floor has been inserted at about half height,
supported on an iron framework.

In 1847, Nos 4, 5 and 6 Slips were provided with cast-

**Covered
Slipways:
HEW 1608
TQ 759 695**

**Iron framed
workshops:
HEW 1609
TQ 763 699**

Chatham Dockyard No. 8 Machine Shop

and wrought iron framed roofs clad with recently developed galvanised corrugated iron sheeting carried on trussed purlins. Frames are spaced 30 ft apart over the 300 ft lengths and are in the form of circular braced arches of 85 ft main span, springing from the tops of 29 ft high cast-iron columns. Side aisles vary in width. The structures were built by George Baker and Son, civil engineering and building contractors.

No. 7 Slip Roof was designed by G. T. Greene, a Royal Engineer on the Admiralty Staff and was completed in 1855. The frames are aligned with the adjoining Baker roofs but the shed is one frame longer. There is a main span of 82 ft, two side aisles spanning 34 ft and a height over the slip of 69 ft. Bracing is by cast-iron lattice type beams and the corrugated iron roof is carried on wrought iron trusses and purlins.

A few years later, a very similar iron structure was built over No.5 Slip at Woolwich Dockyard. It was dismantled in 1869, when Woolwich was closed, and re-erected as the PROM (EW) Factory, a machine shop, at Chatham. The building was 290 ft by 142 ft, 88 ft high and had an 82 ft main span with two side spans of 30 ft each. The cast-iron columns were either 27 in. or 21 by 12 in. in section and were spaced in rows 29 ft apart with wrought iron lattice girders giving longitudinal and lateral bracing. One column had cast into it 'Henry Grissell London

1860'. The roof was supported by N Type wrought iron trusses with diagonal bracing. Cladding to the building was by corrugated sheeting with window lights. Despite being Listed Grade II, the building was demolished in December 1992. The two other listed buildings which had been moved from Woolwich at the same time, remain. The Boiler Shop, built by Fox Henderson and Company between 1847–48, is of very similar size and construction to the PROM (EW) factory but has a distinctive clock tower. No.8 Machine Shop was the oldest of the Woolwich buildings to be moved. Constructed by Fox Henderson around 1845 it is smaller than the other two, being 218 ft long by 118 ft wide and 64 ft high, with a main span of 72 ft and two side spans of 22 ft each. Its largest cast-iron columns are 24 in. by 12 in. in section spaced 14 ft apart. From the main columns wrought iron jib struts support the roof's triangulated trussing. The design of this building appears to be identical with that of two iron slipway roofs constructed at Pembroke Dock in 1844, which have been demolished.

1. COAD J. G. *Historic Architecture of Chatham Dockyard, 1700–1850.* National Maritime Museum, Greenwich, 1982, 180–183.

2. SUTHERLAND R. J. M. Shipbuilding and the long-span roof. *Trans Newcomen Soc.*, 1988–89, **60**, 107–126.

11. Gravesend's Piers: The Town Pier and The Royal Terrace Pier

After much long and sometimes bitter Parliamentary and local wrangling, extending over nearly 20 years, Gravesend Corporation overcame the opposition of local watermen and obtained powers to construct the Town Pier[1] in 1833. This enabled the substantial numbers of ferry passengers from both London and Tilbury to land directly. It was designed by William Tierney Clark and completed by contractor William Wood in July 1834. The approach is 127 ft long, 40 ft wide and comprises three spans carried on cast-iron cross arched ribs. These are supported by iron columns resting on brick and stone foundations which were constructed at low tide. The T-head is 73 ft by 30 ft and its 6 ft deep bearing beams are supported on 18 cast-iron columns, each resting on three

The Town Pier:
HEW 1440
TQ 648 745

The Royal Terrace Pier:
HEW 1441
TQ 651 745

Gravesend Royal Terrace Pier

piles which were driven by a novel method from a temporarily positioned wooden platform. A circular iron shell was initially driven, a hole for the pile was then made with an auger. The pile was inserted, part driven and finally driven after the removal of the shell. The pier was provided with timber decking, ornate ironwork and a red night-light mounted on a 30 ft high tapering cast-iron column of base diameter 3 ft. Later the pier was roofed by the London, Tilbury and Southend Railway Company and survives in this condition as a Grade II listed structure.

In 1835, a committee of residents had constructed a temporary wooden pier as part of the development of the Terrace Gardens, sited a short way downstream of the Town Pier. The temporary structure was replaced in 1844, by the Royal Terrace Pier[2] built by Fox Henderson to the design of John Baldry Redman. The approach was 200 ft by 30 ft and the T-head 90 ft by 30 ft. Columns tapering from 4 ft to 3 ft were set on brickwork and concrete foundations. These, too, had been constructed by a novel method involving the sinking of 6 ft diameter cast-iron cylinders as miniature coffer-dams. Cast-iron girders, 3 ft deep and up to 55 ft long, were placed on top of the columns to carry cross beams and timber decking and to support the superstructure, including a roof of very similar design to New Cross railway station. Extension works were carried out in 1895 and restoration works in 1977–8.

1. CLARK W. T. Account of the Gravesend Pier. *Trans Instn Civ. Engrs*, 1842, **3**, 245–256.

2. REDMAN J. B. Account of the new cast-iron pier at Milton-on-Thames, next Gravesend, in the county of Kent. *Min. Proc. Instn Civ. Engrs*, 1845, **4**, 222–250.

12. Kingsferry Vertical Lift Bridge ♣

HEW 34

TQ 914 693

In 1860, the London, Chatham and Dover Railway (HEW 1760) opened a combined single rail track and road bridge across the tidal River Swale to provide access to the Isle of Sheppey. The bridge's opening bascule span was replaced by a Scherzer rolling lift bridge in 1904, giving a 57 ft navigational passage. The present lift bridge[1] was designed by Mott, Hay and Anderson and was completed in 1960 by contractors John Howard, in association with Dorman Long (Steelwork) and Sir William Arrol (Machinery). Its overall width, of about 50 ft, includes a road carriageway, footpath and single rail track. On each side of the opening span there are three fixed side spans, each about 80 ft wide, connecting to

Kingsferry Lift Bridge

hollow concrete box abutments. The 123 ft long vertical lift opening span provides a navigational width of 90 ft. The two main girders are riveted steel, with welded stringers acting compositely with a 7 in. thick reinforced concrete deck under the carriageway. This is replaced by steel decking under the footpath and the railway is carried on longitudinal timber beams with a steel deck.

The two reinforced concrete main piers comprise twin 32 ft diameter concrete cylinders spaced 56 ft apart and founded in blue clay, at a depth of about 50 ft. An 8 ft 6 in. service tunnel connects the main piers. Four reinforced concrete tapering lifting towers, of height 103 ft 4 in., enable the lifting span, balanced by four 110 ton counterweights, to be raised 95 ft above mean high water. Lift is achieved by twin 120 h.p., d.c. electric winches which can vary the speed of lift from 4 to 64 ft/minute.

1. ANDERSON J. K. and BROWN C. D. Design and construction of the Kingsferry lifting bridge, Isle of Sheppey. *Proc. Instn.Civ. Engrs, 1964,* **28**, 449–470.

♦

HEW 738

TQ 909 752

13. Sheerness Boat Store

The Grade I Listed four storey boat store[1] at Sheerness dockyard is 210 ft long, 135 ft wide and 53 ft high to its ridges. Completed in 1860, it was constructed by Henry Grissell of Regents Canal Ironworks to the design of Col. Godfrey Greene, the Admiralty's Director of Engineering and Architectural Work. The width is divided into three equal sections with the centre open nave being flanked by two four-storey sections. This enabled boats to be brought into the nave, lifted and traversed into the required position on one of the side floors. Varying section, cast-iron, H-columns are supported on pile foundations on a 30 ft by 15 ft grid. These are connected by 18 in. deep longitudinal wrought iron girders of rivetted construction and 12 in. deep, cast-iron traverse beams. Timber traverse beams at 7 ft 6 in. centres contribute to the support of the timber floor, although the ground floor is a concrete slab. The roof trusses are supported on 24 in. deep longitudinal beams. The boat store, which was extraordinarily advanced for its age, relies for its structural stability on joint stiffness, not bracing, and can be

regarded as a very early example, if not the first, multi-storey iron framed building.

Sheerness Boat Store

1. SKEMPTON A. W. The boat store, Sheerness (1858–60) and its place in structural history. *Trans Newcomen Soc.*, **32**, 1960, 57–78.

14. The Canterbury and Whitstable Railway and Tyler Hill Tunnel

The 6 mile long Canterbury and Whitstable Railway[1,2] was proposed by William James in 1823 and a Parliamentary Act for its construction, together with a harbour at Whitstable, was obtained in 1825. Work started in 1826 under the direction of George Stephenson with Joseph Locke and John Dixon as assistants. The line opened in May 1830 and was the country's first passenger and freight railway. It had a single track with passing loops, many steep gradients and an 828 yd long tunnel at a gradient of 1 in 56 at Tyler Hill. Initially the line was worked by a combination of two winding engines, a locomotive (the Invicta) and horses. A third winding engine was installed in 1832 because the Invicta proved incapable of hauling trains on the steeper gradients. Tyler Hill Tunnel, outside Canterbury, was driven in clay and lined with four brickwork rings. It was not built to

The Canterbury and Whitstable Railway: HEW 476 TR 145 583 to 110 670

Tyler Hill Tunnel: HEW 488 TR 141 599

consistent dimensions, being segmental in shape at one end and horseshoe shaped at the other with a minimum height above rail level of 12 ft.

In 1844 the line was leased by the South Eastern Railway (SER) (HEW 1448), who laid heavier rails and changed to locomotive operation throughout. However, the restricted tunnel height required that only specially adapted engines could be used. The railway was bought out by the SER in 1853, carried passenger traffic until 1930 and closed entirely in 1952.

Some sections of the old trackway remain but much has reverted to farmland and, particularly at the Canterbury and Whitstable ends, there has been considerable building development. Tyler Hill Tunnel has been partly filled in with fly ash, following a collapse and subsistence under some of the buildings of the University of Kent in 1974.

1. MAXTED I. *The Canterbury and Whitstable Railway.* The Oakwood Press, Lingfield, 1970.

2. MARSHALL C. F. D. *A History of the Southern Railway.* Southern Railway Company, London, 1936, 11–21.

15. Canterbury Cathedral Water Supply

♦

HEW 1449

TR 152 579

Sited on the north side of the Cathedral, there is a small octagonal water tower with a conical roof. It is 24 ft across with 4 ft walls and 25 ft high eaves and was built in about 1160 by Prior Wibert as part of his water supply scheme for the Cathedral and adjoining Christchurch Priory.[1,2]

Wibert took his supply from springs in Old Park about 1 mile to the north-east. From the source, collecting pipes were laid to a conduit house (TR 163 587) with settling tanks and a primitive filter to supply a 2½ in. diameter lead pipe falling 32 ft at 1 in 100 and passing through five settling tanks, the fifth adjacent to St Gregory's Church. The pipe passes through the grounds of the Priory of St Gregory, which was served by a branch pipe. In return for this service, the Canons gave a basket of apples each September to the monks of Christchurch. From the water tower, pipes supplied a laver on the first floor which acted as a supply for a second water tower; this, in turn, supplied other draw off points. The lavers had seven or eight washing points with the waste water draining into a shallow tank below and thence into a 3 ft square masonry culvert known as Wibert's Great Drain. This ran north to the town ditch and still carries surface water from the Cathedral. An accurate coloured plan of the whole of the original system made at the time of construction is held by the library of Trinity College, Cambridge.

Inevitably many alterations have been made since Wibert's time. In 1668, the Dean and Chapter had the system overhauled to give better distribution to the buildings and a new conduit house was provided in Old Park. This was reconstructed in 1812 and still delivers non-potable water.

1. Hayes J. Prior Wibert's Waterworks. *Canterbury Cathedral Chronicle*, 1977, **71**, 17–26.

2. Tatton-Brown T. The Precincts Water Supply. *Canterbury Cathedral Chronicle*, 1983, **77**, 43–52.

16. Royal Harbour Ramsgate, Dry Dock and No. 1 Slipway

A Board of Trustees was established by Parliamentary Act in 1749 for the construction of a harbour of refuge at Ramsgate.[1,2] Although work commenced the following year, the harbour was not substantially completed until 1792. Two breakwaters enclosed the 46 acre harbour area, the east ultimately about 625 yd long, the west 520 yd, with an entrance width of nearly 70 yd. An extension of 112 yd to the east breakwater had changed the direction of opening from around south-south-east, to nearly south-south-west in order to alleviate wave disturbances in the harbour. The breakwaters have heartings of rammed chalk mixed with gravel and lime mortar and are founded on chalk. Although some Whitby sandstone was used, they are faced mainly with Portland stone with granite copings. At a typical section the top width is 25 ft with side slopes of 1 to 5. The top is set 12 ft 6 in. above high water level with a 3 ft 6 in. parapet wall. The works, initially designed by William Etheridge, commenced under the direction of mason Thomas Preston but it was soon found that substantial quantities of sediment accu-

Royal Harbour:
HEW 484

Dry Dock:
HEW 1322

No 1. Slipway:
HEW 1321

TR 385 647

Ramsgate Harbour, excavation of Smeaton Dry Dock. Courtesy of R. B. Martin

mulated within the harbour. John Smeaton's advice was sought in 1774 and he was appointed Engineer from 1778 until his death in 1792. In conjunction with Preston, Smeaton proposed an inner basin with a lock entrance and six sluices to flush out the harbour at low tide. This was based upon a method employed in the Low Countries and proved successful at Ramsgate.

Smeaton designed a dry dock, sited at the eastern end of the inner basin. It was 100 ft long, nearly 31 ft wide and 15 ft deep. A timber floor on wooden piles was specified to be built before the masonry walls. The floor design was changed to a flat inverted masonry arch by Henry Cull but, after completion it failed, because the hydraulic uplift pressure caused sideways thrust on the walls resulting in serious cracking. The dock was then successfully rebuilt to Smeaton's design using timber piles and floor beams held down by the weight of the walls and was opened in 1791. The dock was extended by 20 ft in 1815 and remained in use for 80 years. It was converted to an ice store and filled in but has now been excavated and part restored.

The harbour's repair capability was enhanced in 1838

Ramsgate
Harbour

with the construction of No.1 Slipway in accordance with Morton's patent. The 40 ft wide ramp is constructed of granite setts at a slope of 1 in 16 with a length of 300 ft above low water. It is provided with three sets of double rails, nearly 11 ft apart, which carry a wheeled cradle capable of taking vessels of up to 500 tons. An electrically driven winch hauls the cradle instead of the original manual capstan.

Today, the inner basin is a yacht marina and there are moorings in the outer harbour for fishing vessels. Port Ramsgate, a cross channel ferry terminal, has been constructed on reclaimed land to the west. Its breakwaters enclose the old harbour.

1. SKEMPTON A. W. (Ed.) *John Smeaton FRS*. Thomas Telford, London, 1981,206–216.

2. MATKIN R. B. The construction of Ramsgate Harbour. *Trans. Newcomen Soc.*, 1977, **48**, 1977, 53–71.

17. North Foreland Lighthouse ♣

It is believed that a light may have existed at North Foreland, Broadstairs from the early sixteenth century.

HEW 733

TR 399 698

North Foreland
Lighthouse

In 1634, Sir John Meldrum was given powers to collect dues from passing shipping. Fire damaged the light tower in 1683 and the succeeding coal-fired beacon, built ten years later, was also lost for the same reason. The keepers were paid £13 per year with a free cottage and coal and on calm nights were expected to keep the light bright by use of bellows.

Around the start of the eighteenth century an octagonal tower was built of brick and stone. The open light was coal fired and an attempt between 1719 and 1730 to enclose it was unsuccessful because of difficulties in cleaning the glass. Open fires continued to be used until 1790 when the tower was reconstructed increasing the height to 64 ft 7 in. Parts of the existing structure were retained. The light was about 187 ft above mean high water and was provided by eighteen Argand oil lamps with reflectors and lenses. Trinity House undertook the lighthouse's management in 1832. It now has an intensity of 175 000 candle power and a range of 21 miles.

18. Dover Harbour

♦

HEW 125

TR 330 410

Dover's geographical position on the south-east corner of England has always ensured its harbour's importance as a continental link.[1] Remains have been found of the Roman harbour at the mouth of the River Dour. Accretion due to littoral drift gradually forced the harbour towards the sea under the shelter of the Western Heights, where the Wellington and Granville Docks and Tidal Harbour exist today. Protection was afforded by a rocky promotory, which Henry VIII ordered to be extended by the construction of a pier. However, this caused shingle banks to form in its lee, obstructing the entrance.

In 1840 a Royal Commission recommended that a large deep water harbour of refuge be constructed in Dover Bay. Work commenced in 1847 with the letting of

Dover Harbour. Courtesy of Dover Harbour Board

Dover Harbour under construction

a contract for the first 800 ft of the 2100 ft long Admiralty Pier. Completed in 1871, this was built of 7 to 8 ton concrete blocks faced with stone. It gave protection against south-westerly gales and inhibited siltation of the harbour quays. The South Eastern Railway (HEW 1448) ran tracks alongside the ferry berths on the eastern side. Protection against easterly winds was achieved by the 1650 ft long Prince of Wales Pier, constructed between 1892 and 1902 to the design of Coode, Son and Mathews. The pier was provided with rail tracks for boat trains and had at its landward end an iron and steel viaduct which permitted water circulation within the harbour. Concurrently with this work, the Admiralty constructed a 640 acre Admiralty Harbour with an average water depth at low tide of 30 ft; the designers were again Coode, Son and Mathews.[2] The work, completed in 1909, comprised a 2942 ft long eastern breakwater, a 2000 ft extension of the Admiralty Pier and the 4212 ft South Island breakwater. This provided two harbour entrances of 670 ft to the east and 740 ft to the west. The breakwaters were constructed of concrete blocks weighing between 26 and 41 tons laid on the hard chalk bottom. The blocks were faced with granite to 4 ft below the low water mark. At the harbour's eastern end 21 acres of land were reclaimed and 3910 ft of sea-wall constructed.

Opposite: Dover Pharos

1. HASENSON A. *The history of Dover harbour*. Aurum Special Editions, London, 1980.

2. WILSON M. F-G. Admiralty Harbour Dover. *Min. Proc. Instn Civ. Engrs*, 1919–20, Part 1, **209**, 31–112.

19. Dover Pharos ♣

HEW 478

TQ 326 418

The Romans erected two lighthouses on the cliff tops at Dover. Only the foundations remain of the one sited on the west cliff, which was built perhaps in the third century. The Pharos, probably dating from the first century, is sited within Dover Castle and its surviving octagonal

tower has a side length of 14 ft and is about 34 ft across at the base.[1] There is a square interior and the walls are about 10 ft thick. It is believed originally to have been about 80 ft high and constructed in eight stages, each stage having its vertical face stepped back about a foot from the one below, giving a telescopic outline. The Roman construction is of flint rubble cased in tufa ashlar with bonding courses of imported red tile brick. The materials are cemented with salmon coloured Roman mortar. Around the start of the eleventh century, the Church of St Mary-in-Castro was built alongside and the Pharos became a free standing bell tower. Of the remaining stages, only the lower four are Roman. The topmost stage of 19 ft is of fifteenth century construction.

1. BROWN R. A. *Dover Castle, Kent.* MPBW Historic Buildings and Ancient Monuments, London, 1966, 37–38.

20. Channel Tunnel Works

HEW 477

TR 270 385 to 300 395

Channel Tunnel boring machine

Although a channel tunnel proposal was made in 1802, it was not until 1874 that Francis Brady, acting for the Channel Tunnel Company, recommended an alignment which was approved by both French and British authorities. A length of 33 miles of railway was proposed at a cost of £10 million, exclusive of rolling stock. Preliminary borings were made to depths of 567 ft at St Margaret's Bay and 500 ft on the French coast. Work was suspended

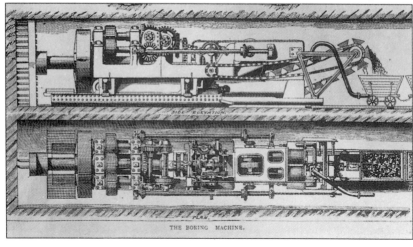

THE BORING MACHINE.

because of the Franco-Prussian war but recommenced with a shaft being sunk at Abbot's Cliff and a tunnel commenced from the shaft. It was abandoned in 1881 after 879 yd had been driven. In the same year the South Eastern Railway (SER) (HEW 1448) obtained Parliamentary powers for further work. Brady, now the SER's Chief Engineer, directed the construction of a shaft sunk at the west end of Shakespeare Cliff, from which a 7 ft diameter tunnel was driven for 2025 yd before work was stopped in 1882. A rotary tunnelling machine designed by Beaumont was used for both tunnels but was abandoned in the second. A model of the machine is in the Science Museum, Kensington.

The project was revived in the 1960s and work commenced with the intention of driving twin rail tunnels with a service tunnel between. Entrance to the works was adjacent to the west portal of Shakespeare Cliff Tunnel (HEW 485). This project was curtailed in 1975. Yet a further revival occurred in the 1980s, again involving twin rail tunnels and a service tunnel. Extensive progress has been made with the service tunnel being initially driven by December 1990. At time of publication, the tunnels were completed and expected to be commissioned in 1994.

21. Folkestone Warren, Abbotscliff Tunnel and Shakespeare Cliff Tunnel

Between Folkestone and Dover, the South Eastern Railway (HEW 1448) crossed an area of undercliff called Folkestone Warren. It is a zone of extensive and deep seated landslips. Records of slips date back to 1765 and since the railway construction, in 1844, ten incidents have interrupted railway traffic. The most serious was in 1915 when almost the whole 2 miles of the Warren moved seawards by up to 50 yd. The railway was not reopened until 1919. The landslips have been extensively investigated[1] and considerable remedial works have been undertaken.[2] These include the construction of a sea-wall and groynes along the Warren's length, the weighting of the central 500 yd length and the driving of numerous headings into the slide masses to improve drainage.

Folkestone Warren:
HEW 1669
TR 242 375 to 268 385

Abbotscliff Tunnel:
HEW 1393
TR 268 385 to 285 389

Shakespeare Cliff Tunnel:
HEW 485
TR 303 397

Immediately to the east of the Warren, the Abbotscliff Tunnel[3] was constructed between 1840 and 1844. It is 1933 yd long, 24 ft wide and 19 ft 6 in. high. Driven through chalk it has a six-ring brick arch lining throughout. The alignment was close to both the cliff face and high tide level, which enabled an unusual construction method to be employed. In addition to a number of conventional vertical shafts, side shafts were driven into the cliff face from a road running along the cliff base. These were used for spoil disposal into the sea. A substantial spring, the Lydden Spout, burst through at one point and had to be incorporated into the tunnel drainage.

Again to the east is the 1392 yd Shakespeare Cliff Tunnel[3]. It was perceived that the chalk was of poorer quality than that relating to the Abbotscliff tunnel and consequently adjacent twin gothic arched tunnels were designed. They are brick-lined, 12 ft wide and separated by a pier some 10 ft thick. There is a large clearance of about 28 ft between rail and peak. There are seven vertical ventilation shafts which have a maximum depth of about 240 ft and these coincide with horizontal construction shafts driven from the sea shore.

Shakespeare Cliff.
Courtesy of
British Rail

1. Muir Wood A. M. Folkestone Warren landslips, investigations 1948-50. *Proc. Instn Civ. Engrs*, 1955, Part 2, **4**, 410–428.

2. VINER-BRADY N. E. V. Folkestone Warren landslips, remedial measures, 1948–54. *Proc. Instn Civ. Engrs*, 1955, Part 2, **4**, 429–466.

3. BLOWER A. *British railway tunnels*. Ian Allan, London, 1964, 60–61 (Abbotscliff), 81–82 (Shakespeare Cliff).

22. Folkestone Harbour and East Pier ♣

Folkestone Harbour[1] is based on the natural haven at the valley in the cliffs where the Pent Stream enters the sea. In 1807 an Act was passed, based on plans by William Jessop, authorising the formation of a Harbour Company financed by the Loan Commission. Thomas Telford, who was an adviser to the Commission, became involved with Folkestone Harbour and subsequently acted as a consultant.

Folkestone Harbour: HEW 1859

East Pier: HEW 1446

TR 235 360

In 1808 work commenced on a 14 acre harbour, which was smaller than originally proposed. The harbour walls are believed to be an innovative design by Telford[2] and were constructed by laying undressed slabs, up to two tons in weight, at roughly 45° to the horizontal. They were laid in two rows with the interior being filled with broken stone. The west pier extended 400 ft seawards and then turned at right angles to the east to form the 950 ft long South Pier parallel to the shore. To give protection from easterly winds another pier was built from the shore for a distance of 700 ft and formed a 120 ft wide entrance. The East Pier can be seen today, much the same as when it was built. It is 15 ft wide and on average 5½ ft above mean high water. Similarly in the Inner Basin the west and south quay faces show the original construction.

The harbour was completed about 1820 but it soon became silted because it intercepted the easterly flowing littoral drift. Telford advised on keeping the harbour silt free, but his scheme was not carried out because it was considered too expensive by the Harbour Company. The Company became bankrupt in 1842 and the following year the harbour was purchased by the South Eastern Railway (SER) (HEW 1448).

By 1843 the SER had arrived at Folkestone and, although it did not run to the harbour, it established a steamer service to Boulogne. A coal jetty was built and was connected to the main line at Folkestone Junction by a 1325 yd tramway at a gradient of 1 in 36. This was converted to carry passengers and in 1849 trains were able to terminate at a Harbour Station built on reclaimed land to the south of the Harbour and made accessible by a swing bridge.

Piecemeal harbour development ensued on reclaimed land, with the provision of improved station facilities, a customs hall, covered platforms and railway sidings. A new harbour arm, extending in a south-easterly direction from the centre of the original South Pier was built in the century's latter decades. It is 1480 ft long, constructed on concrete blocks faced with granite and has a lighthouse at its end. In 1972 roll-on, roll-off road vehicle facilities were provided. Conventional ferry services finished at the end of 1991, but since then a catarmaran service has started.

1. BISHOP C. H. *The story of a town.* Headley Bros, London, 1973, 79–97.

2. SMILES S. *Lives of the engineers: Metclalfe and Telford.* Murray, London, 1874, 210–11.

♣

HEW 482

TR 227 364

23. Foord Viaduct Folkestone

The yellow brick Foord Viaduct[1] dominates the skyline of Old Folkestone. It is the only major bridging structure on the South Eastern Railway's route from London to

Dover (HEW 1448). Its 757 ft total length conveys the tracks over nineteen semicircular arches each comprising four brick rings. The maximum height from ground level to arch soffit is 78 ft and the piers taper in elevation. There are plain, solid but somewhat shallow, parapets which assist in giving a well proportioned appearance. One hundred years after the viaduct's completion in 1843, the structural stability was improved by the insertion of six longitudinal tie rods at springing level of each span. It is a Listed Grade II structure.

1. BIDDLE G. and NOCK O. S. *The railway heritage of Britain*. Joseph, London, 1983, 186.

24. Folkestone Cliff Railway

HEW 1165

TR 225 355

The Leas funicular cliff railway[1] was the first of its type to be built on the south coast. It was designed by Reginald Pope, constructed by Waygood and Company of South-wark and opened in September 1885 to carry passengers the 100 ft between the cliff top and the lower promenade.

There are two fourteen-person carriages mounted on four wheeled triangular framed trucks, which give a level floor, because the track is angled at 40° to the horizontal. Each carriage runs on a separate 5 ft 10 in. gauge track and they are coupled together by steel wire ropes passing around a large pulley wheel at the upper terminal. In order to operate the lift, water is admitted to the ballast tanks of the upper carriage; this overcomes the weight of the lower one which is drawn up as the upper carriage descends. Control is achieved by a brake on the pulley wheel although emergency brakes are fitted to each carriage.

Due to passenger demand a second lift was constructed in 1890. Space limitations resulted in a slightly different design but it operated in the same manner. Demand fell in the 1950s and, following an accident, it was taken out of service around 1960. The Leas lift is now owned and operated by the Shepway District Council and the lower terminal, containing ticket office, waiting room, pump room and offices is a Listed Building.

1. HART B. *Folkestone's cliff lifts*. Milgate Publishing Company, Uckfield, 1985.

Opposite: Foord Viaduct

Folkestone Cliff
Railway

25. Romney Marsh Reclamation, Dymchurch Sea-wall and Royal Military Canal

The area of Romney and adjacent marshes is bounded by Hythe to the north-west, Rye and Winchelsea to the south-west and the promontory at Dungeness. It lies to the south of a broken arc of low hills running from Hythe to Rye and encompasses an area some 20 miles by 10 miles. It is now largely grazing land which has been progressively drained since Roman times[1], when the Rhee Wall running between the present locations of

Appledore and New Romney formed its southern boundary.

Originally the River Rother discharged into the sea at Hythe. By 1250 a channel running adjacent to the line of the Rhee Wall had been constructed, into which the Rother was diverted. This enabled New Romney to be developed as a port. However, when sea surges caused a further southwards diversion of the Rother to flow past Iden and Rye, New Romney estuary rapidly silted, which closed the port.

About 5 miles to the north-east of New Romney a 3½ mile length of coast has been protected for many centuries by the Dymchurch sea -wall. Sea protection in the area is believed to date from Roman times and its early construction was an earth bank reinforced with brushwood, especially blackthorn. There is evidence of maintenance work in Henry VIII's reign and in 1803 John Rennie was consulted on the wall's condition. In the 1820s and 1830s the wall was faced with Kentish Ragstone quarried from the Hythe area and this was followed by the construction of a 1 in 7 apron with timber toe piling.[2] Further work on the apron and toe was required in 1892, at which time authorisation was granted for the provision of a series of lightweight groynes. More recent works include some Welsh granite facing, undertaken in the 1930s and grouting and concrete facing work to the apron in the early 1960s.

The marsh is bounded to the north by the 22½ mile long Royal Military Canal, which runs from a lock on the River Rother near Iden to a sea sluice at Hythe.[3] It was designed by John Rennie, constructed in 1806 and was originally for military purposes at a time when the French threatened invasion. From 1810 it was used by commercial traffic which rapidly declined with the opening of the South Eastern Railway's Ashford to Hastings line in 1851. However, the canal has continued to be used as a drainage channel with several pumping stations constructed along its length to drain the marsh's northern levels.

Romney Marsh Reclamation:
HEW 848
TQ 89 14 to
TR 16 35

Dymchurch Sea-Wall:
HEW 1249
TR 090 270 to
130 320

Royal Military Canal:
HEW 488
TQ 936 244 to
TR 188 349

1. ROBINSON G. W. Land drainage and sea defences of Romney Marsh. *Cantium*, Summer 1972, Part 2, **4**, 33–41.

2. ELLIOTT J. Dymchurch Wall. *Min. Proc. Instn Civ. Engrs*, 1847, **6**, 466–484.

3. VINE P. A. L. *The Royal Military Canal.* David and Charles, Newton Abbot, 1972.

26. Dungeness Lighthouses: 1792, 1904 and 1961

♣

Constructed
1792:
HEW 1164

Constructed
1904:
HEW 479

TR 089 169

Constructed
1961:
HEW 480

TR 094 169

The promontory at Dungeness has always been a hazard to shipping. Shingle transported along the coast from Rye Bay has steadily moved the point eastwards. There have been at least five lighthouses but the site of the earlier two cannot be located accurately.

The first known light was provided as a result of Sir Edward Howard receiving a patent from King James I in 1615 for an open coal fire to be financed by a shipping toll. In 1635, William Lamplough, who had taken over the patent rights, dismantled the first tower and built a more substantial tower with open coal fire, closer to the receding shoreline.

Further changes in the coastline by 1792 resulted in Samuel Wyatt constructing a third brick tower which reproduced the shape of Smeaton's Eddystone Light. It was 116 ft high and lit by eighteen sperm oil lamps. When inspected by Robert Stephenson in 1818, parabolic reflectors were found to be in use. In 1862, Dungeness was one of the first English lighthouses to be fitted with an electric light but this was subsequently replaced by an 850 candle power oil lamp surrounded by glass prisms.

Yet again coastline changes necessitated a new light which was completed by Messrs Patrick of London in 1904. It was 136 ft high, 38 ft in diameter at the base and now stands about 1500 ft from high water. Its effectiveness was seriously inhibited in 1960 with the construction of an adjacent nuclear power station which obstructed the light shining into Rye Bay. Consequently, in 1961, the current lighthouse was constructed nearly 1500 ft to the east. It is 130 ft high, 12 ft in diameter and is constructed of 'vertically stressed', precast concrete rings. Its Xenon electric arc lamp has an intensity of 1.92 million candle power and a range of 27 miles.

Opposite:
Dungeness
Lighthouse, 1904.
1906 lighthouse
in background

27. Union Mill Cranbrook ♣

HEW 467

TQ 779 359

Union Mill is a white painted octagonal smock mill on a brick base sited in the centre of Cranbrook. It is 75 ft high and was built in 1814 by James Humphrey for Henry Bobell. It had simple cloth-covered sweeps which were dangerous to reef in strong winds. In 1840, William Medhurst, a Lewes millwright, installed a new windshaft and four 68 ft sweeps with feathering mechanisms constructed in accordance with William Cubitt's patent of 1807. The cloth strips were replaced by a number of small wooden shutters pivotted at either end. This allowed them to be feathered by the manual operation of a system of rods and cranks by means of a looped chain hung from a pulley. Adjustments could be made while the sweeps were rotating. A six-blade Sussex fantail mechanism was also added to keep the sweeps facing the wind.

A steam engine was installed in 1863 and electric drive in 1954. The mill was owned by the Russell family from 1832 to 1958 when it was acquired by Kent County Council. They overhauled it in 1959 and replaced the sweep's pitch pine stocks by welded steel hollow rectangular sections.

♣

Scarlett's Dam:
HEW 1841
TQ 443 401

Furnace Mill
Dam :
HEW 605
TQ 455 399

28. Cowden Dams: Scarlett's Dam and Furnace Mill Dam

Three dams were built across the valley of the Kent Water Stream in the sixteenth century to provide power for the Wealden iron industry. Only the upper two remain. Scarlett's dam, with a downstream height of 15 ft 6 in., is 203 ft long and 15 ft wide at the top and holds back a lake of three acres. It carries a track approximately 8 ft wide. At the south end there are the remains of a three-bay sluice with timber peg paddle gear. The water level in the lake is currently maintained by a weir constructed in the late 1970s.

The dam was breached by a flood in 1968 exposing a section of 60 ft base width and 20 ft depth. It appears that the original dam, built around 1571, was 4 ft high and constructed of clay to serve a furnace and forge. It had subsequently been raised 4 ft using clay and furnace clinker. A wooden outlet pipe and sluice were found in these early works. There had been two further height increases by the mid-eighteenth century. After the cessation of iron working, a corn mill was established in the late eighteenth century and the dam was raised 7 ft with a 2 ft thick stone facing on the upstream side. Evidence has been found of a gun casting pit, wheel pit and tail race, together with the remains of a water-wheel.

Downstream is Furnace Mill Dam which retains a lake of 30 acres and has a downstream height of about 15 ft. It is 375 ft long, 15 ft wide at the top and carries a public road. A new overflow weir was provided as part of repair work necessitated by the 1968 flood. A map of 1748 shows a gun boring house, adjacent to the dam, which became a corn mill and is now a private dwelling. The first floor was level with the dam road, enabling corn to be carried easily into the mill.

Opposite: Union Mill Cranbrook

29. Bewl Bridge Reservoir and Dam ♣

HEW 1636

TQ 685 334

The works were completed in 1975 to augment the water supply to Maidstone, the Medway towns and surrounding areas. Water is fed from the reservoir into the River Teise, which joins the Medway and is extracted at Springfield, 1 mile above the tidal limit at Allington Lock.

The reservoir, which is one of Britain's largest, has a catchment area of 7 sq. miles but most of its water is pumped from the River Teise in the wet season. The reservoir's surface area is 1.2 sq. miles, its capacity is around 6 000 million gallons and it floods three converging valleys.

The earth dam,[1] 3 136 ft long and 105 ft high, is con-

261

structed of local material. It has a clay core and blanket of Wadhurst clay. Because of variations in thickness of the underlying Wadhurst clay, the cut-off trench is offset near the dam's upstream toe. It is filled with a bentonite gravel slurry.

The circular reinforced concrete draw off tower is 118 ft high and has an internal diameter of 21 ft. Access is by a 740 ft long, 11 ft diameter tunnel through the dam, then up the tower by an internal electric lift. Overflow relief is provided by a second reinforced concrete tower, with a spillway designed to accept over 25 000 gallons/second.

The designers for the work were Southern Water Authority and Rofe Kennard and Lapworth, consulting engineers. Gleeson Civil Engineering were the Contractors.

1. INTERNATIONAL COMMISSION ON LARGE DAMS: BRITISH NATIONAL COMMITTEE. *Dams in the U.K. 1963–1983.* BNCOLD, London, 1983, 44–45.

30. Rye Ancient Water Supply

HEW 1166

TQ 922 203

In 1730, the Mayor and Jurats of Rye invested £600 to improve their water supply by the construction of a high level cistern,[1] fed by a piped supply from springs in the

Rye Water
Cistern

Ashdown sands. The cistern was sited in the churchyard of St Mary's church, the highest point in the town. Water was pumped through the 80 ft rise to the cistern via a 2 in. diameter elm pipe. The pump on the northern side of the town was driven by a horse gin. It was installed in 1718 and the supply cistern was completed in 1735. Relics of the old pump may be seen at the foot of Conduit hill.

The Grade II Listed brick cistern is oval in plan with axes of 30 ft and 20 ft and has a dished floor about 3 ft below ground level. Its capacity is 20 000 gallons with a water depth of 8 ft. An oval brick tower, about 17 ft by 9 ft in plan, is founded on the floor and supports the elliptical brick arch roof, through which it protrudes by 10 ft. The roof of the tower is tiled with a dressed lead ridge resembling an upturned boat in overall shape.

1. WOOD R. The remarkable cistern at Rye. *Sussex Industrial History*, **7**, 1976, 24–28.

Site index

Additional sites

The Scilly Isles, West and Central Cornwall

Goonhilly Radio Telescope
(HEW 1456, SW 727 213)

Gribbin Day Mark, Gribbin Head
(HEW 1804, SX 098 497)

Liskeard and Looe Railway
(HEW 1534, SX 254 538 to 235 643)

Moorswater Viaduct, Masonry
(HEW 796, SX 237 640)*

Penadlake Viaduct
(HEW 872, SX 135 650)

Penzance Timber Viaduct
(HEW 874, SX 482 311)*

Resprynn Bridge, R.Fowey
(HEW 1562, SX 099 634)

Roundwood Quay
(HEW 645, SW 838 404)*

St Agnes Lighthouse
(HEW 883, SV 877 083)

St Anthonys Head Lighthouse
(HEW 884, SW 846 311)

St Germans Viaduct
(HEW 869, SX 364 573)

The Tamar Valley and Plymouth

Higher Bridge, Nr Launceston
(HEW 1564, SX 349 867)

Laira Bridge, Plymouth
(HEW 340, SX 501 542)

Leemoor Tramway Bridge
(HEW 1466, SX 520 568)

Central and Eastern Devon

Barnstaple Railway Bridge
(HEW 634, SS 56 33)

Bickleigh Bridge (HEW 1866, SS 937 077)

Broad Clyst– Cullompton Turnpike
(HEW 1844, SX 985 990 to ST 019 064)

Causeway and Arches, Clyst St Mary
(HEW 1093, SX 972 911)

Countess Wear Bridge, Exeter
(HEW 1803, SX 942 895)*

Dainton–Hemerdon Banks, S.Devon Rly
(HEW 1360, SX 874 694 to 537 565)

Prince of Wales Pier, Penzance
(HEW 1896, SW 807 330)

Dawlish to Teignmouth Sea Wall
(HEW 793, SX 979 779 to 946 732)

Exe Bridge, Nr. Dulverton (HEW 1934, SS 929 245)

Exeter, New North Road Entrance
(HEW 1847, SX 923 928 to 912 940)

Exeter–Tedburn St Mary Highway
Diversion (HEW 1827,
SX 895 914 to 816 941)

Exeter–Barnstaple Rd
(HEW 1845, SX 768 025 to 586 247)

Exeter–Tiverton Turnpike (HEW 1846,
SX 909 953 to 938 974)

Exmouth Sea-wall (HEW 1916,
SX 994 806 to 060 804)

Haytor Granite Tramway (HEW 1054,
SX 75 77 to 85 74)

Holbeam Wood Dam (HEW 1176, SX 826 717)

Ilfracombe Harbour (HEW 1490, SS 525 477)

Ilfracombe Wind Tunnel Generator
(HEW 1622, SS 505 465)

Ivybridge Viaduct (HEW 875, SX 635 568)*

Land Reclamation, Budleigh Salterton
(HEW 1273, SY 07 82)

Lynmouth Bridges (HEW 1451, SS 724 496)

Marley Tunnel (HEW 1355, SX 718 606 to 727 606)

Seaton Harbour Bridge (HEW 615,
SY 252 900)

Shaldon Bridge (HEW 1761, SX 932 725)

Sidmouth Promenade Wall (HEW 1863, SY 123 871 to 129 873)

St Thomas Viaduct, Exeter (HEW 1350, SX 914 919)*

Starcross Atmospheric Pumping Station (HEW 792, SX 977 817)*

Start Point Lighthouse (HEW 1370, SX 828 372)

Tumbling Weir, Ottery St Mary (HEW 1177, SY 095 953)

Turnpike Era Road, Minehead–Bampton (HEW 1935, SS 955 421 to 933 243)

Turnpike Era Road, Tiverton - Bampton (HEW 1936, SS 954 125 to 933 141 and 960 221)

West Charleton Land Reclamation (HEW 1453, SX 749 416)

Wivelscombe Turnpike (HEW 1933, SS 74 25 to ST 07 27)

Somerset and mid-Wiltshire

Allermoor Pumping Station Museum (HEW 1410, ST 357 307)

Ashton Windmill, Chapel Allerton (HEW 919, ST 414 504)

Bascule Bridge, Bridgwater (HEW 1526, ST 298 375)*

Bottle Bridge, Hatch Beauchamp (HEW 1515, ST 300 195)

Bow Bridge, Bruton (HEW 1141, ST 683 347)

Brean Close Sluice (HEW 1408, ST 308 562)*

Cheddar Structural Test Centre (HEW 1162, ST 463 544)

Crimson Hill Tunnel (HEW 1473, ST 311 221)*

Crossways Bridge, Bridgwater (HEW 1517, ST 309 352)

Currymoor Pumping Station (HEW 1411, ST 344 288)

Donyatt North Bridge, Nr Chard (HEW 1516, ST 339 138)

Easton Bridge (HEW 1312, ST 510 481)

Haselbury Bridge (HEW 1513, ST 459 110)

High Bleadon Bridge, Uphill (HEW 1079, ST 327 581)*

Hinkley Point Power Station (HEW 1215, ST 210 460)

Hurstbow Bridge, Martock (HEW 657, ST 458 189)

Iron Bridge, Mark (HEW 1142, ST 376 480)

Langport, Somerton and Castlecary Turnpikes (HEW 1310, ST 32 to 63)

Load Bridge, Nr Martock (HEW 1512, ST 467 238)

Marsh Bridge, Dulverton (HEW 1405, SS 907 289)

Maud Heath's Causeway (HEW 680, ST 972 737 to 919 739)

Mendip Television Mast, Penhill, (HEW 1540, ST 564 488)

New Cut Bridge, Taunton (HEW 1510, ST 250 257)*

Nynehead Court Drive Aqueduct (HEW 1551, ST 144 218)

Parrett Works, Martock (HEW 1347, ST 445 187)

Pinkworthy Pond Dam, Exmoor (HEW 1588, SS 723 423)

Rockwell Green Water Tower (concrete) (HEW 1521, ST 126 201)

Rockwell Green Water Tower (Brick) (HEW 1522 ST 126 201)

Sea Wall, Blue Anchor, Somerset (HEW 1365, ST 021 434 to 033 435)

Stembridge Mill, High Ham (HEW 1346, ST 433 305)

Telescopic Bridge, Bridgwater (HEW 1109, ST 300 374)*

Tone Bridge, Creech St Michael (HEW 1511, ST 273 253)

Tone Aqueduct, Chard Canal (HEW 973, ST271 253)

Tone Aqueduct, Grand Western Canal
(HEW 1552, ST 147 224)

Trefusis Bridge, Grand Western Canal
(HEW 1404, ST 166 232)

Waterloo Bridge, Shepton Mallet
(HEW 1524, ST 619 438)

Wells Cathedral, Scissors Arches
(HEW 1013, ST 552 459)

Westford Pumping Station
(HEW 1523, ST 123 205)

Westonzoyland Pumping Station
(HEW 1409, ST 338 329)*

Whiteball Tunnel (HEW 1547, ST 090 180)*

Wookey Hole Caves Hydro Electric Station
(HEW 1416, ST 531 478)

Dorset and South Wiltshire

Canford Magna Suspension Bridge
(HEW 898, SZ 030 988)

Julian's Bridge, Wimborne (HEW 897,
SZ 004 998)

Swanage Pier (HEW 1634, SZ 036 787)

Wool Ancient Bridge (HEW 375, SY 844 872)

Hampshire and the Isle of Wight

Basingstoke Canal (HEW 1575, TQ 055 620
to SU 640 523)*

Beaurepaire Bridge (HEW 652, SU 644 584)

Cromwell's Dock, Portsmouth
(HEW 372, SU 628 007)

Eastney Pumping Station (HEW 504,
SZ 672 993)

Hurstbourne Viaduct
(HEW 506, SU 430 489)*

Medina Drawbridge, Isle of Wight
(HEW 635, SZ 50 88)

No. 3 Ship Shop, Portsmouth (HEW 1042,
SU 628 008)

Norris Bridge, Twyford (HEW 651,
SU 477 247)

R.Meon Canal, Sea Lock, etc.
(HEW 1633, SU 532 027 to 542 058)

Seaview Pier, Isle of Wight
(HEW 716, SZ 63 93)

Shawford Viaduct (HEW 509, SU 475 265)

Southampton Water Supply - Artesian Well
(HEW 1580, SU 416 138)

Sussex and South Surrey

Eastbourne Pier
(HEW 431, TV 617 988)

Ford Retractable Bridge, 1844
(HEW 1692, TQ 004 042)

Ford Retractable Bridge, 1862
(HEW 1693, TQ 004 042)

Frith Hill Water Tower, Godalming
(HEW 1467, SU 969 447)

Hardham Tunnel (HEW 496, TQ 033 172 to
TQ 033 176)

Hastings West Hill Cliff Lift
(HEW 1447, TQ 822 096)

Newhaven Swing Bridge (HEW 268,
TQ 447 014)

Nutley Windmill
(HEW 1478, TQ 451 291)

Shalford Watermill, Surrey
(HEW 1356, TQ 001 476)

Treadmill Crane, Guildford (HEW 1486,
SU 994 495)*

Volks Railway, Brighton (HEW 500,
TQ 315 035 to 333 033)*

Wey and Arun Canal (HEW 1574,
SU 948 467 to TQ 069 259)*

Worthing Pier (HEW 1270, TQ 149 023)

Kent

Brook Horse Gin (HEW 1352, TQ 066 443)

Canal Swing Bridge, Gravesend (HEW
1326, TQ 676 740)

Chart Gunpowder Mill, Faversham
(HEW 1323, TR 010 615)

Chatham Dockyard Artesian Well
(HEW 1593, TQ 767 698)

Cripps Corner Bridge
(HEW 1325, TQ 776 212)

Deal Pier (HEW 715, TR 380 525)

London and Greenwich Railway

(HEW 1725, TQ 330 800 to 392 779)*
Loose Bridge (HEW 1324, TQ 759 521)

Maidstone Bridge (HEW 1671, TQ 757 555)

Miers Court Horse Gin
 (HEW 1318, TQ 814 645)

Outwood Windmill
(HEW 1357, TQ 328 456)

Saltwood Tunnel
 (HEW 1320, TR 153 365 to 161 369)

Swanscombe Cutting Footbridge
(HEW 1670, TQ 598 726)

*These works are referred to in the text.

Bibliography

Abbott W. *The turnpike road system in England and Wales 1663–1840.* Cambridge University Press, 1972.

Adamson S. H. *Seaside piers.* Batsford, London, 1977.

Addis W. *Structural engineering: the nature of theory and design.* Ellis Horwood, Chichester, 1990.

Bainbridge C. *Pavilions on the sea, a history of the seaside pier.* R. Hale, London, 1986.

Barbey M. F. *Civil engineering heritage: Northern England.* Thomas Telford, London, 1981.

Beaver P. *A history of lighthouses.* Peter Davies, London, 1971.

Beckett D. *Brunel's Britain.* David and Charles, Newton Abbot, 1980.

Beckett D. *Stephenson's Britain.* David and Charles, Newton Abbot 1984.

Berridge P. S. A. *The girder bridge.* Robert Maxwell, London, 1969.

Biddle G. and Nock O. S. *The railway heritage of Britain.* Joseph, London, 1983.

Biddle G. *The railway surveyors: the story of railway property management 1800 –1990.* I.Allan, London, 1990.

Biddle G. *Victorian stations, railway stations in England and Wales, 1830–1923.* David and Charles, Newton Abbot, 1973.

Binnie G. M. *Early Victorian water engineers.* Thomas Telford, London, 1981.

Binnie G. M. *Early dam builders in Britain.* Thomas Telford, London, 1987.

Blower A. *British railway tunnels.* Ian Allan, London, 1964.

Body G. *Railway stations of Britain.* Patrick Stephens, Wellingborough, 1990.

Booker F. *Industrial archaeology of the Tamar valley.* David and Charles, Newton Abbot, 1967.

Bourne J. C. *The history and description of the Great Western Railway.* Bogue, London, 1864; reissued David and Charles, Newton Abbot. 1970.

Bracegirdle B. *The archaeology of the Industrial Revolution.* Heinemann, London, 1973.

Brees S. C. *Railway practice*, 2nd series. John Williams, London, 1846.

British bridges. Public Works, Roads and Transport Congress, London, 1933.

Brunel I. *The life of Isambard Kingdom Brunel, civil engineer.* Longman, London 1870; reissued David and Charles, Newton Abbot, 1971.

Burton A. *The railway builders.* J. Murray, London, 1992.

Carter E. F. *An historical geography of the railways of the British Isles.* Cassell, London, 1959.

Charlton T. M. *A history of structures in the nineteenth century.* Cambridge University Press, 1982.

Chrimes M. M. *Civil engineering 1839 – 1889: a photographic history.* Alan Sutton, Stroud, 1991.

Coad J. G. *The royal dockyards 1690– 1850.* Scolar Press, Aldershot, 1989.

Collins A.R. (ed.). *Structural engineering: two centuries of British achievement.* Tarot Print, Chislehurst, 1983.

Conder F. R. *Personal recollections of English engineers.* Hodder and Stoughton, London, 1868. Reissued as *The men who built railways*, Thomas Telford, London, 1983.

Cossons N. and Trinder B. *The Iron Bridge.* Moonraker Press, Bradford-on-Avon, 1979.

Cossons N. *The BP book of industrial archaeology.* David and Charles, Newton Abbot, 1975.

Course E. *London's railways*. Batsford, London, 1962.

Course E. *The railways of southern England. 2 Vols*. Batsford, London, 1973–74.

Cresy E. *Encyclopaedia of civil engineering*. Longman, London, 1856.

Day J. R. and Wilson B. G. *Unusual railways*. Fredrick Muller, London, 1957.

de Maré E. *Bridges of Britain*. Batsford, London, 1975.

de Vesian J. S. E. and Gueritte T. J. *Hennebique reinforced concrete: theory and practice*. L. G.Mouchel, London, 1921.

Dempsey G. D. *Tubular and other iron bridges*. Virtue Bros., 1864; reissued Cass, London, 1970.

Devereux R. *John Loudon McAdam: chapters in the history of highways*. Oxford University Press, London, 1936.

Fairbairn W. *The application of cast iron and wrought iron to building purposes*. Weale, London, 1857.

Fairclough A. *The story of Cornwall's railways*. Tor Mark Press, Truro.

Fowler C. E. *The ideals of engineering architecture*. Spon, London, 1929.

Hadfield C. *British canals: an illustrated history*. David and Charles, Newton Abbot, 1979.

Hadfield C. *The canals of southern England*. Phoenix, London, 1955.

Hadfield C. *The canals of south west England*. David and Charles, Newton Abbot, 1967.

Hadfield C. *The canal age*. David and Charles, Newton Abbot, 1981.

Hadfield C. *The canals of south and south east England*. David and Charles, Newton Abbot, 1969.

Hadfield C. and Skempton A.W. *William Jessop, Engineer*. David and Charles, Newton Abbot, 1979.

Hague D. B. and Christie R. *Lighthouses, their architecture, history and archaeology*. Gomer Press, Llandyssul, 1975.

Harris H. *The industrial archaeology of Dartmoor*. David and Charles, Newton Abbot, 1968.

Harris R. *Canals and their architecture*. Godfrey Cave, London, 1980.

Henderson C. and Jervoise E. *Old Devon bridges*. Wheaton, Exeter, 1938.

Henderson C. and Coates H. *Old Cornish bridges*. Simpkin Marshall, London, 1928; reissued Bradford Barton, Truro, 1972.

Hewitt C. A. *English historic carpentry*. Phillimore, Chichester, 1980.

Heyman J. *The masonry arch*. Ellis Horwood, Chichester, 1982.

Hinde T. *Capability Brown*. Hutchison, London, 1986.

Humber W. *Cast iron and wrought iron bridges and girders for railway structures*. Spon, London, 1857.

Jackson D. *Lighthouses of England and Wales*. David and Charles, Newton Abbot, 1978.

Jackson A. A. *London's termini*. David and Charles, Newton Abbot, 1969.

Jensen M. *Civil engineering around 1700*. Danish Technical Press, Copenhagen, 1969.

Jervoise E. *The ancient bridges of the south of England*. Architectural Press, London, 1930.

Jones E. *The Penguin guide to the railways of Britain*. Allen Lane, London, 1981.

MacDermot E. T. and Clinker C. R. *History of the Great Western Railway*. Vol.1: 1833–63; vol.2: 1863-1921. Ian Allan, London, 1964.

Macdougall P. *Royal dockyards*. David and Charles, Newton Abbot, 1982.

Margary J. D. *Roman roads in Britain*. John Baker, London, 1973.

Margary J. D. *Roman ways in the Weald*. Phoenix House, London, 1948.

Marshall C. F. D. *A history of the Southern*

Railway. Southern Railway Company, London, 1936.

Marshall J. *The Guinness book of rail facts and feats.* Guinness Superlatives, Enfield, 1979.

Nock O. S. *The railway engineers,* Batsford, London, 1955.

Pannell J. P. M. *An illustrated history of civil engineering.* Thames and Hudson, London, 1964.

Penfold A. (ed.). *Thomas Telford: engineer.* Thomas Telford, London, 1980.

Pevsner N. *The buildings of England - Cornwall.* Penguin, Harmondsworth, 1951.

Price F. *A treatise on carpentry.* C. Ackers, 1759.

Priestley J. *Navigable rivers, canals and railways throughout Great Britain.* Longman, London, 1831.

Pugsley Sir A. (ed.). *The works of Isambard Kingdom Brunel: an engineering appreciation.* Institution of Civil Engineers and University of Bristol, London and Bristol, 1976.

Reader W. J. *Macadam: The McAdam family and the turnpike roads 1798-1861.* Heinemann, London, 1980.

Rennie Sir J. *British and foreign harbours.* Weale, London, 1854.

Rennie Sir J. *The autobiography of Sir John Rennie.* Spon, London, 1875.

Richards Sir James M. *The National Trust book of bridges.* Cape, London, 1984.

Rolt L. T. C. *Isambard Kingdom Brunel.* Pelican, London, 1972.

Rolt L. T. C. *George and Robert Stephenson.* Pelican, London, 1978.

Ruddock E.C. *Arch bridges and their builders 1735 - 1835.* Cambridge University Press, Cambridge, 1979.

Simms F.W. *Practical tunnelling.* Crosby Lockwood, London, 1844.

Simms F. W. *The public works of Great Britain.* Weale, London, 1838.

Singer C. et al. *History of technology.* 5 Vols. Oxford University Press, Oxford, 1954– 58.

Sivewright W.J. (ed.). *Civil engineering heritage: Wales and western England.* Thomas Telford, London, 1986.

Skempton A.W. *British civil engineering, 1640 - 1840: a bibliography of contempory reports, plans and books.* Mansell, London, 1987

Skempton A.W.(ed.). *John Smeaton FRS.* Thomas Telford, London, 1981.

Smith N. *A history of dams.* Peter Davies, London, 1971.

Stephens J. H. *The Guinness book of structures.* Guinness Superlatives, Enfield, 1976.

Straub H. *A history of civil engineering.* Leonard Hill, London, 1952. 4th German Edition, Birkhauser, Basel, 1992.

Telford T. (Rickman J. (ed.)). *Life of Thomas Telford.with a folio atlas of copper plates.*London, 1838.

Thomas D. St J. *West country railway history.* David and Charles, Newton Abbot, 6th edn 1988.

Timoshenko S. P. *History of the strength of materials.* McGraw-Hill, London, 1953. Reissued Dover Publications, 1983.

Turner J. H. *The London Brighton and South Coast Railway.* 3 Vols. Batsford, London, 1977-79.

Vaughan A. *Isambard Kingdom Brunel: engineering knight errant.* John Murray, London, 1991.

Wallis A. J. *Dorset bridges, a history and guide.* The Abbey Press, Sherbourne, 1974.

Walmisley A.T. *Iron roofs.* Spon, London, 1888.

Walters D. *British railway bridges.* Ian Allan, London 1963.

Webb S. and Webb B. *English local government: the story of the King's highway.* Longmans, 1913; reissued Frank Cass, London, 1963.

White H. P. *A regional history of the railways of Great Britain. Vol 2: southern England.* David and Charles, Newton Abbot, 1992.

Williams R. A. *The London and South*

Western Railway. 2 Vols. David and Charles, Newton Abbot, 1968–73.

Whishaw F. *The railways of Great Britain and Ireland.* Simpkin Marshall, London, 1840; reissued David and Charles, Newton Abbot, 1969.

Woodfin R. J. *The centenary of the Cornwall railway.* Jefferson, Ely, 1960.

Wright G.H. *Bridges of Britain: a pictorial survey.* D Bradford Barton, Truro, 1973.

Wryde J. S. *British lighthouses.* Unwin, London, 1913.

Yeomans D. T. *The trussed roof: its history and development.* Scolar Press, Aldershot, 1992.

Metric equivalents

Imperial measurements have been used in giving dimensions of the works described, as this system was used in the design of the great majority, except for modern structures where the appropriate metric units are given.

The following are metric equivalents of the Imperial units used.

Length	1 inch = 25.4 millimetres
	1 foot = 0.3048 metre
	1 yard = 0.9144 metre
	1 mile = 1.609 kilometres
Area	1 square inch = 645.2 square millimetres
	1 square foot = 0.0929 square metre
	1 acre = 0.4047 hectare
	1 sqare mile = 259 hectares
Volume	1 gallon = 4.546 litres
	1 cubic yard = 0.7646 cubic metre
Mass	1 pound = 0.4536 kilogram
	1 UK ton = 1.016 tonnes
Pressure	1 pound force per square inch = 6.895 kilonewtons per square metre = 0.06895 bar
Power	1 horse power = 0.7457 kilowatt

Name Index

Engineers

Subject index

Lighthouses

Railway Stations

Reclamation (See Sea Defences)

Reservoirs (See Dams)

Roads